CHRISTIAN SCIENCE HYMNAL

Hymns 430–603

The Christian Science Publishing Society
Boston, Massachusetts, USA

Christian Science Hymnal
Hymns 430–603

The Church Dome and Tower Medallion is a trademark of The Christian Science Board of Directors and is registered in the United States.

ISBN 978-0-87510-504-8 Pew Edition
ISBN 978-0-87510-505-5 Musician's Edition

Printed in the USA
21 20 19 18 17   2 3 4 5

PREFACE

In *Colossians, we read,* "Let the word of Christ dwell in you richly in all wisdom; teaching and admonishing one another in psalms and hymns and spiritual songs, singing with grace in your hearts to the Lord" (3:16). The enduring power of hymns to inspire, teach, praise, and heal truly has ancient origins. It is with deep joy and resounding gratitude that we present this *Christian Science Hymnal: Hymns 430–603*, which is the most significant infusion of new hymns into our repertoire in more than eighty years. Building on the 2008 *Christian Science Hymnal Supplement*, it joins, but does not replace, the 1932 *Christian Science Hymnal* as a source of comfort, joy, and inspiration. The hymns presented here are available not only for church services, Sunday School, and other forums for congregational singing, but also for individual prayer and study.

The first *Christian Science Hymnal* was published in 1892. It contained 193 distinct hymn texts, close to 300 hymn tunes, and included three of Mary Baker Eddy's poems. Five more hymnals followed over the succeeding forty years, adding four more poems by Mrs. Eddy along the way. The preparation of the 1932 *Hymnal* involved the collection and evaluation of existing hymns, as well as the solicitation of contributions from Christian Scientists from all over the world. That same model was followed in the preparation of this hymnal, which brings together a panorama of hymns from 43 countries across six continents.

The Range of Christian Science Hymns

This compilation reflects the two priorities that were paramount in its development: metaphysical clarity and musical excellence. The result is a hymnal designed to meet the needs of all earnest seekers for Truth. The universal reach of divine Science can be seen in the diverse array of countries that originated hymns contained in the 1932 *Hymnal*, and that global expansiveness continues in the present volume. The distinct, sometimes musically disparate, hymns included in this collection remind us of the following sentence from *Science and Health with Key to the Scriptures* by Mary Baker Eddy: "All the varied expressions of God reflect health, holiness, immortality — infinite Life, Truth, and Love" (p. 518).

Editorial Standards

This hymnal is the result of countless considerations, deliberations, and decisions. The *Manual of The Mother Church* states: "The music in The Mother Church shall not be operatic, but of an appropriate religious character and of a recognized standard of musical excellence; it shall be played in a dignified and suitable manner" (Mary Baker Eddy, p. 61). The attributes of joy, excellence, dignity, and "appropriate religious character" are evidenced in the spiritual depth and musical integrity of this volume. As hymnody continues to evolve, new favorites will join beloved classics in strengthening the worship experience of our church services.

Full-Score Appendix and Indexes

To ensure the ease of use of this hymnal for congregations, page turns are avoided by presenting longer hymns in a simplified version, showing the melody and words only. The complete hymn, including the accompaniment, can be found in the Full-Score Appendix. The index of authors, composers, and sources, and the alphabetical listing of first lines and common titles, are useful for locating hymns. Of special interest to musicians are the alphabetical and metrical listings of the hymn tunes.

Acknowledgments

Profound gratitude is owed to the numerous individuals and committees who contributed their time, expertise, and artistry to this project. We are grateful for the contributions of authors and composers, many of whom graciously permitted revision of their work to ensure the consistency, unity, and accessibility of the collection. In addition to those acknowledged within these pages, scores of people ushered this process from the call for submissions to publication. Music arrangers, historians, translators, consultants, volunteers, editors, and proofreaders were essential to the completion of this project. We are grateful for the collaboration and consultation of specialists in hymn publishing, whose expertise and experience have been invaluable. In addition, we appreciate the ready help of members and fellows of the Hymn Society of the United States and Canada, as well as the services of many scholars, librarians, and archivists.

These hymns provide a source of spiritual sustenance, whether experienced through the shared joy of congregational singing or through the holy consecration of individual prayer. "Whatever inspires with wisdom, Truth, or Love — be it song, sermon, or Science — blesses the human family with crumbs of comfort from Christ's table, feeding the hungry and giving living waters to the thirsty" (*Science and Health*, p. 234).

The Christian Science Board of Directors

A Grateful Heart a Garden Is   430

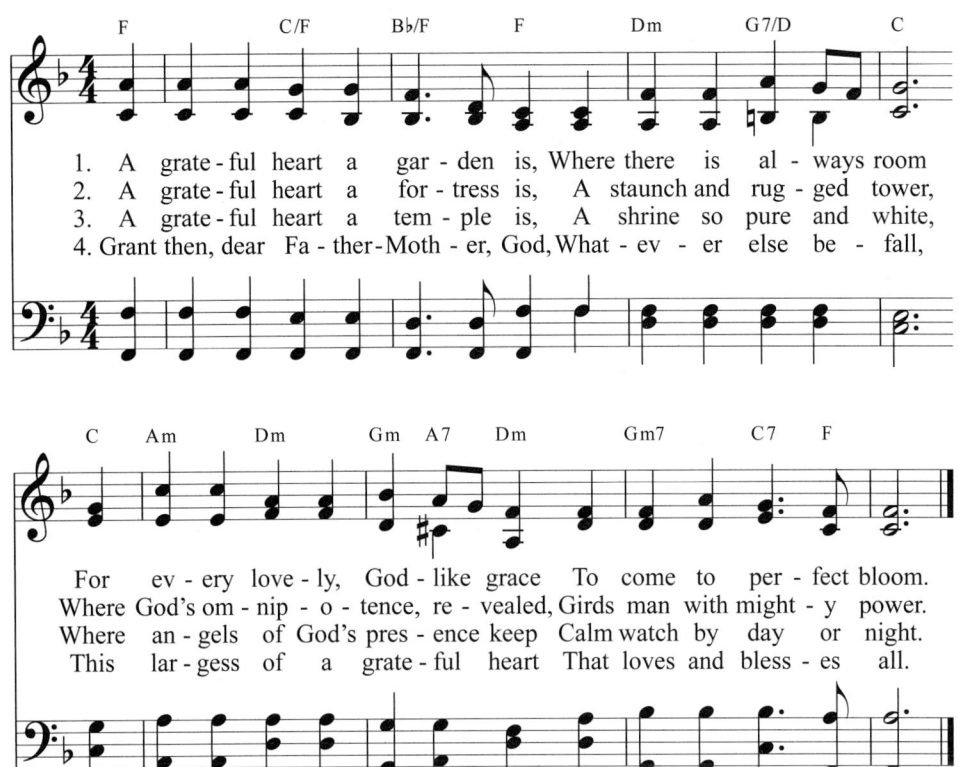

1. A grate-ful heart a gar-den is, Where there is al-ways room
2. A grate-ful heart a for-tress is, A staunch and rug-ged tower,
3. A grate-ful heart a tem-ple is, A shrine so pure and white,
4. Grant then, dear Fa-ther-Moth-er, God, What-ev-er else be-fall,

For ev-ery love-ly, God-like grace To come to per-fect bloom.
Where God's om-nip-o-tence, re-vealed, Girds man with might-y power.
Where an-gels of God's pres-ence keep Calm watch by day or night.
This lar-gess of a grate-ful heart That loves and bless-es all.

WORDS: Ethel Wasgatt Dennis, alt.
MUSIC: James R. Corbett
Words © 1932, ren. 1960 The Christian Science Board of Directors
Music © 2017 The Christian Science Board of Directors

LARGESS OF HEART
C.M.
Alternate tune: 3

431 A Holy Air Is Breathing Round

1. A holy air is breathing round,
A fragrance from above:
Be every thought from sense unbound,
Be every action love.

2. O God, unite us heart to heart,
In sympathy divine,
That we be never drawn apart,
To love not Thee nor Thine;

3. But by the life of Jesus taught,
And all his gracious word,
Be nearer to each other brought,
And nearer Thee, O Lord.

WORDS: Abiel Abbot Livermore, adapt.
MUSIC: Benjamin M. Martin

HEILIG LUFT
C.M.
Alternate tune: 4

Above All Earthly Gain

Plutôt que tous les gains

1. A - bove all earth - ly gain, I long to hear and
English 2. When, in hu - mil - i - ty, I feel Your pres - ence
3. Dear Love, rule out the fears From all who flee op -

1. *Plu - tôt que tous les gains, J'as - pi - re à Te con -*
French 2. *Ou - vrant mon cœur, je peux Res - sen - tir Ta pré -*
3. *E - li - mi - ne les peurs De la pla - nè - te en -*

know You, E - ter - nal Mind, To be Your lov - ing
near me, Your peace di - vine, Hope leads me safe a -
pres - sion; Dry up their tears, Our Fa - ther - Moth - er

naî - tre, A - mour di - vin, A re - flé - ter le
sen - ce, Ta paix, mon Dieu, Cet - te fer - me es - pé -
tiè - re, Gué - ris les cœurs, Tout - puis - sant Pè - re -

1, 2

child, To find the lib - er - ty That You a - lone pro - vide.
shore; I know Your love will guard And guide me ev - er - more.
God! Your Word es - tab - lish - es The rule of

bien, Trou - ver la li - ber - té Que Toi seul peux don - ner.
ran - ce: Sa - voir que Ton a - mour Nous gar - de - ra tou - jours.
Mè - re! Ta Pa - ro - le di - vi - ne In - stau - re

3

har - mo - ny; Your good - ness is re - vealed And here for all to see.
l'har - mo - nie, Et Ta bon - té par - fai - te A tout ja - mais s'ac - com - plit.

These words are from a poem, entitled "Migration," written specifically to fit this melody. The music is adapted from Gabriel Fauré's *Cantique de Jean Racine*, a work that earned the composer first prize as a student at the Ecole Niedermeyer in 1865.

WORDS: Josette Flamand, incl. Eng. tr.
MUSIC: Gabriel Fauré; adapt. and arr. CSPS

Irregular

433 A New Commandment

This hymn may be sung twice, with the descant included the second time through.

WORDS: Para. John 13:34, 35
MUSIC: Anon.; arr. and desc. John F. Wilson
Music arr. and desc. © 2017 The Christian Science Board of Directors

NEW COMMANDMENT
Irregular

434 A Village Humble, Still

1. A vil-lage hum-ble, still, A guid-ing star a-bove,
2. The shep-herds brought their faith, The Wise-men of-fered gold

A shep-herd watch-ing on a hill, A moth-er-heart of love—
And cost-ly frank-in-cense and myrrh; Each brought his gift of old.

A child is born of grace, Brings peace to all the earth,
What shall we give to-day? A thing of world-ly worth?

Matthew 2:11 / Luke 2:8–14.

AIRIKAR
S.M.D.

WORDS: Verse 1 Gertrude E. Velguth; verse 2 Kathleen O'Connor; adapt. Adrienne M. Tindall;
further adapt. CSPS
MUSIC: Adrienne M. Tindall; harm. Erik Routley

While an - gels sing their joy - ous praise, And glo - ri - fy his birth.
Or hearts at - tuned to an - gel songs—The gift of our new birth?

435 All Is Done for the Glory of God
Tout est fait pour la gloire de Dieu

English
1. All is done for the glory of God.
2. Life is lived for the glory of God.
3. Wor-ship is for the glory of God.
4. Giv-ing is for the glory of God.

A - men! A - men!

French
1. Tout est fait pour la gloi-re de Dieu,
2. La vie, c'est pour la gloi-re de Dieu,
3. Le cul-te est pour la gloi-re de Dieu,
4. L'of-fran-de est pour la gloi-re de Dieu,

A - men ! A - men !

Ev - 'ry-thing we do is serv-ing our God.
Ev - 'ry-thing we do is lov-ing our God.
Ev - 'ry-thing we do is prais-ing our God.
Ev - 'ry-thing we do is thank-ing our God.

A - men! A -

Tout dé - pend de ce que tu en fais.
Tout dé - pend de ce que tu en fais.
Tout dé - pend de ce que tu en fais.
Tout dé - pend de ce que tu en fais.

A - men ! A -

II Corinthians 4:15. This hymn from Cameroon can be performed as a call-and-response: one group sings the first line, the second group responds with two "amens"; the first group sings the next line, the second group responds with two "amens"; both groups sing together the remainder of the verse.

WORDS: Abel Nkuinji; Eng. tr. S T Kimbrough Jr., adapt. CSPS
MUSIC: Abel Nkuinji

TOUT EST FAIT
9.10.9.Amens

men! A-men!   A - men!   A - men!
men! A-men!   A - men!   A - men!

All   is done for the glo-ry of God.   A - men!   A - men!
Tout est fait pour la gloi-re de Dieu,   A - men!   A - men!

436

All May Seem Vain

Alles ist eitel

English
1. All may seem vain, but we are for-ev-er With
2. Life is e-ter-nal, in-fi-nite light, and It

German
1. Al - les ist ei - tel, Du a - ber bleibst — und
2. Le - ben ist e - wig, un - end-lich gut. — Du

You, writ-ten in the book of Life.
gives us con-vic-tion, strength, and might.

wen Du ins Buch des Le - bens schreibst.
gibst uns Ge-wiss - heit, Kraft und Mut.

You are for-ev - er, You are for-ev - er,
In - fi-nite light, in - fi-nite light,

Du a - ber bleibst, Du a - ber bleibst.
Un - end-lich gut, un - end-lich gut.

I Samuel 12:21, 22 / Psalms 102:12 / Revelation 3:5. This beautiful melody can be sung as a canon, with successive voices entering every eight measures.

WORDS: Verse 1 Gerhard Fritzsche; verse 2 Juliane Klein; Eng. tr. CSPS
MUSIC: Theophil Rothenberg

10.9.10.9.8.9.

437　All My Hope on God Is Founded

1. All my hope on God is found-ed; Day by day my trust is new. Through the trials of life He guides me, On-ly good and on-ly true. God a-lone,

2. Earth-ly trea-sures, pride and glo-ry, Hu-man power and world-ly trust, Though with care and toil are build-ed, In the end will fall to dust. But God's power,

3. Dai-ly does th'al-might-y Giv-er Boun-teous gifts on us be-stow. Love's de-sire our soul de-light-eth, Joy at-tends us where we go. Bless-ings stand

4. Now from man to God e-ter-nal End-less thanks and praise be sung. Hearts made new are an-thems rais-ing Through the love of Christ, His Son. Hear God's call,

WORDS: Joachim Neander; tr. Robert Bridges; adapt. Fenella Bennetts, alt.
MUSIC: Herbert Howells

MICHAEL
8.7.8.7.3.3.7.

Words adapt. © 2008 Fenella Bennetts
Music © 1938 Novello & Co., Ltd.

dear - ly known,	Calls my heart to	be His own.
hour by hour,	Is my tem - ple	and my tower.
at God's hand,	Heal - ing flows at	Love's com - mand.
one and all,	We who fol - low	shall not fall.

438 Amazing Grace

1. A - maz - ing grace! how sweet the sound, That
2. 'Twas grace that taught my heart to fear, And
3. Through man - y dan - gers, toils, and snares, I
4. The Lord has prom - ised good to me, His

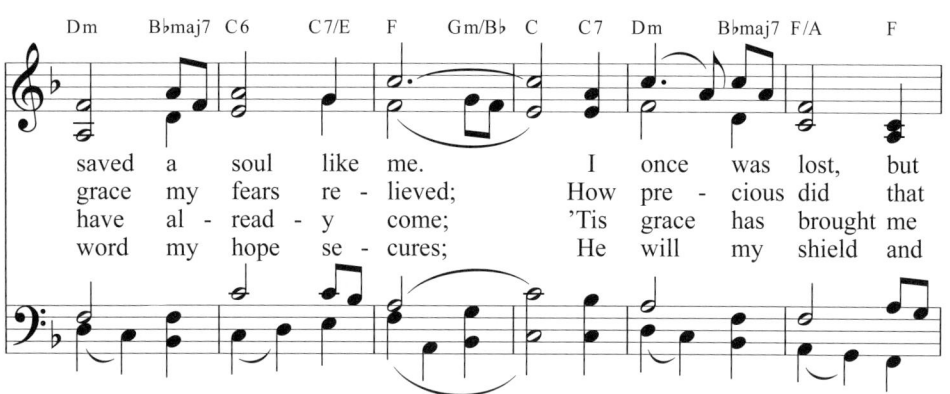

saved a soul like me. I once was lost, but
grace my fears re - lieved; How pre - cious did that
have al - read - y come; 'Tis grace has brought me
word my hope se - cures; He will my shield and

now am found, Was blind, but now I see.
grace ap - pear The hour I first be - lieved!
safe thus far, And grace will lead me home.
por - tion be As long as life en - dures.

A former slave-ship captain, John Newton went on to become a clergyman in the Church of England. Later in life, Newton deeply regretted his involvement in human trafficking; his 1878 pamphlet, *Thoughts Upon the African Slave Trade*, was influential in the abolitionist movement.

WORDS: John Newton, adapt.
MUSIC: American melody, Shaw and Spillman's *Columbian Harmony*, 1829;
   harm. and arr. Robert Rockabrand

NEW BRITAIN
C.M.

As a Fire Is Meant for Burning 439

1. As a fire is meant for burn-ing With a bright and warm-ing flame,
2. As a green bud in the spring-time Is a sign of life re-newed,
3. We are learn-ers; we are teach-ers; We are pil-grims on the way.

So a church is meant for heal-ing Giv-ing glo-ry to God's name.
May we grow as signs of one-ness 'Mid earth's peo-ples, man-y hued.
We are bear-ers of the gos-pel, We are chil-dren of the day.

Not to preach mere creed or cus-tom, But to prove God's lov-ing care,
As a rain-bow lights the heav-ens When a storm is past and gone,
By our gen-tle, lov-ing ac-tions We would show that Christ is light.

We join hands a-cross the na-tions, Find-ing neigh-bors ev-ery-where.
May our lives re-flect the ra-diance Of God's new and glo-rious dawn.
With a hum-ble, lis-tening spir-it We would live to God's de-light.

WORDS: Ruth Duck, adapt.
MUSIC: American melody, White and King's *The Sacred Harp*, 1844; harm. CSPS

BEACH SPRING
8.7.8.7.D.

440 As Sings the Mountain Stream

1. As sings the moun-tain stream,
Past rock and ver-dure wild,
sing my way to You,
Your pure and hap-py

2. O bound-less source of might,
My praise must e'er in-crease,
Life e-ter-nal-ly,
Whose bless-ings nev-er

3. I sing my way to-day,
My heart is joy-ous, free,
Yours is ev-er mine,
Your love is all I

So let me

For Love is

For what is

WORDS: Violet Ker Seymer, alt.
MUSIC: Annette Ruth Söllinger

BERGBACH
S.M.
Alternate tune: 16

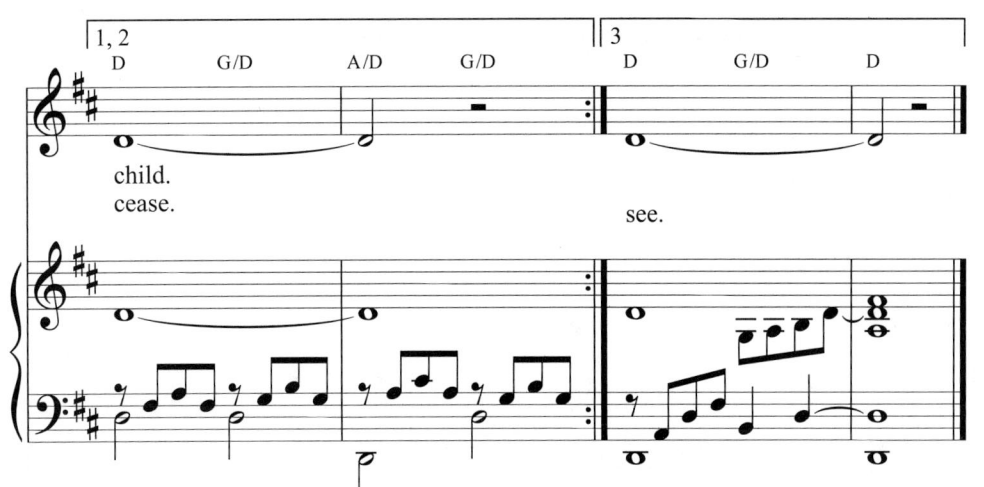

child.
cease.

see.

441 Be Firm and Be Faithful

1. Be firm and be faith-ful; de - sert not the right; The brave be-come bold - er the dark - er the night. Then up and be do - ing, though cow-ards may fail; Thy du - ty pur - su - ing, dare all and pre - vail.

2. If scorn be thy por - tion, if ha - tred and loss, If stripes or a pris - on, re - mem - ber the cross. God watch - es a - bove thee, and He will re - quite; For - sake those that love thee, but nev - er the right.

A copy of the 1898 *Christian Science Hymnal* which Mary Baker Eddy used in her home carries the following note, written in her own hand: "Sing often in The Mother Church the hymn 173" (no. 18 in the 1932 *Hymnal*). That text is presented here with a new musical setting.

WORDS: Anon.
MUSIC: Fenella Bennetts, alt.
Music © 2017 The Christian Science Board of Directors

DAUNTLESS
11.11.11.11.
Alternate tune: 18

Be Thou My Vision

1. Be Thou my vi - sion, O Lord of my heart;
2. Be Thou my wis - dom, and Thou my true Word;
3. Rich - es I heed not, nor earth's emp - ty praise,
4. High King of heav - en, my vic - to - ry won,

Naught be all else to me, save that Thou art.
I ev - er with Thee and Thou with me, Lord;
Thou mine in - her - i - tance, now and al - ways;
May I reach heaven's joys, O bright heav - en's sun!

Thou my best thought, by day or by night,
Thou my great Fa - ther and I Thy true son,
Thou and Thou on - ly, first in my heart,
Heart of my own heart what - ev - er be - fall,

Wak - ing or sleep - ing, Thy pres - ence my light.
Thou in me dwell - ing, and I with Thee one.
High King of heav - en, my trea - sure Thou art.
Still be my vi - sion, O Rul - er of all.

John 17:21. The melody of this hymn was first published in Patrick W. Joyce's *Old Irish Folk Music and Songs* (1909). It was joined to the text given here—also Irish, dating from the 8th century—in *Church Hymnary* (1927), published by the Church of Scotland.

WORDS: Irish, ca. 8th c.; tr. Mary E. Byrne; versed Eleanor H. Hull, alt.
MUSIC: Irish melody, Joyce's *Old Irish Folk Music and Songs*, 1909; harm. Jack Schrader
Music harm. © 1989 Hope Publishing Company

SLANE
10.10.10.10.
Alternate arr.: 485

443 Be Gentle, Be Pure

Sei gütig und rein

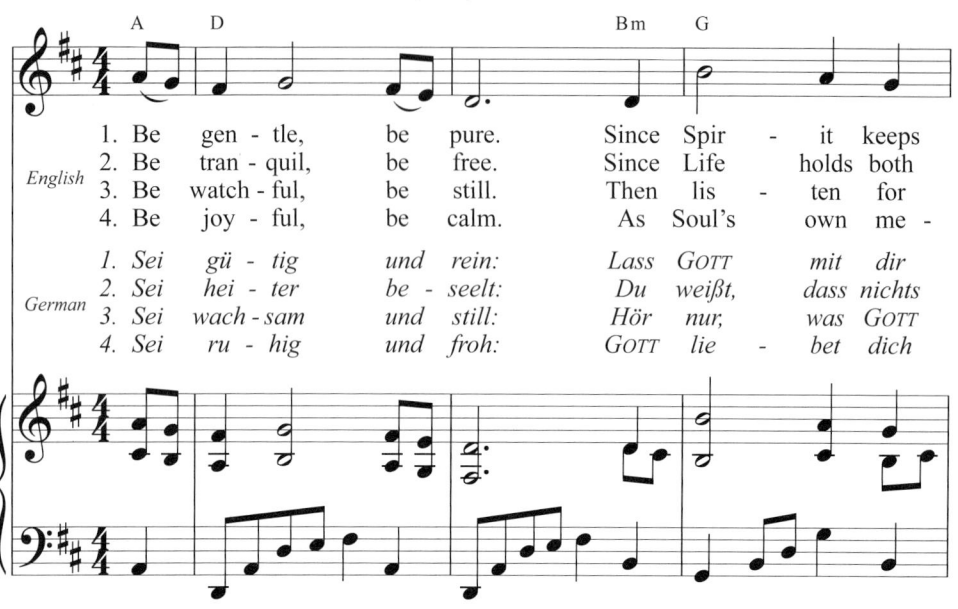

English
1. Be gen - tle, be pure. Since Spir - it keeps
2. Be tran - quil, be free. Since Life holds both
3. Be watch - ful, be still. Then lis - ten for
4. Be joy - ful, be calm. As Soul's own me -

German
1. Sei gü - tig und rein: Lass GOTT mit dir
2. Sei hei - ter be - seelt: Du weißt, dass nichts
3. Sei wach - sam und still: Hör nur, was GOTT
4. Sei ru - hig und froh: GOTT lie - bet dich

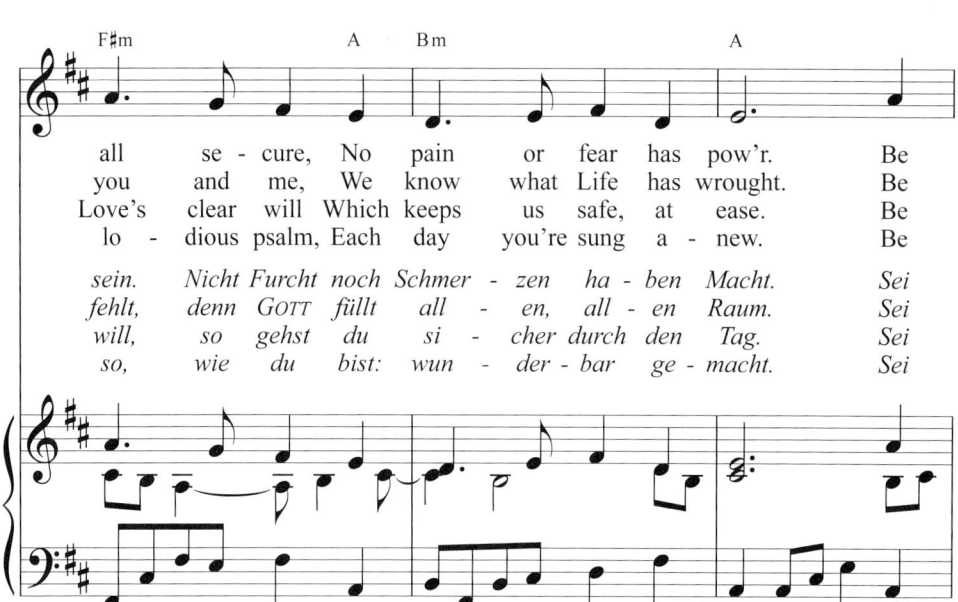

all se - cure, No pain or fear has pow'r. Be
you and me, We know what Life has wrought. Be
Love's clear will Which keeps us safe, at ease. Be
lo - dious psalm, Each day you're sung a - new. Be

sein. Nicht Furcht noch Schmer - zen ha - ben Macht. Sei
fehlt, denn GOTT füllt all - en, all - en Raum. Sei
will, so gehst du si - cher durch den Tag. Sei
so, wie du bist: wun - der - bar ge - macht. Sei

Psalms 46:10 / II Timothy 2:24 / James 3:13–18.

WORDS: Juliane Klein; Eng. tr. CSPS
MUSIC: Juliane Klein

5.7.6.5.6.6.

Ger. Words, Eng. tr., Music © 2016 The Christian Science Board of Directors

Be Still, My Heart

1. Be still, my heart: you rest in Love di-vine; God's gra-cious touch has si-lenced grief and pain. Love's time-less Christ al-lows for no de-cline; In change-less be-ing shall your health re-

2. Be still, my heart: of pres-ent glo-ries sing, In-stead of mourn-ing for a trou-bled past. Re-place sad tunes with mel-o-dies that ring Of God's rich mer-cy and of bless-ings

3. Be still, my heart: our God casts out all fears, As-sur-ing you that God and man are one; And in that one-ness here and now ap-pears Love's ev-er-last-ing life, with death out-

The words to this hymn were first published in the July 1987 issue of *The Christian Science Journal.*

WORDS: Harold Rogers, alt.
MUSIC: Fenella Bennetts

ASSURANCE
10.10.10.10.10.10.

main. Be still, my heart: your faith-ful on - ly
vast. Be still, my heart: the winds and waves re -
done. Be still, my heart: no lies, no tears, no

Friend Se - cures your joy - ful voy - age with - out end.
cede When to God's an - gel voic - es you give heed.
curse Can mar the rhy - thm of God's u - ni - verse.

445

Be Thou, O God

Communion Doxology

Be Thou, O God, ex - alt - ed high; And as Thy glo - ry fills the sky,

So let it be on earth dis-played, Till Thou art here and now o-beyed.

Danish

O Du, vor Gud, ophøjet vær.
Som Du i himlen herlig er,
vis og Din herlighed på jord,
til alle lyder her Dit ord.

Dutch

O God, ons loflied rijze omhoog,
Uw licht omstraalt de hemelboog,
Zo love de aard Uw heerlijkheid,
Van nu aan tot in eeuwigheid.

Finnish

Sun kunniaasi julistaa
nyt Herra, taivas sekä maa.
Ylistys Sulle soikohon
ja tahtos tapahtukohon!

French

Gloire au Très-Haut, à l'Éternel !
Que sur la terre, comme au ciel,
Le règne de notre Seigneur
Soit établi dans tous les cœurs !

German

Wir preisen Dich, GOTT, unsren Herrn!
Dein Ruhm erfüllt die Himmel fern.
Lass leuchten ihn auf Erden hier,
Dass alle Welt gehorche Dir.

Greek

Κύριε, η δόξα Σου τρανή
καθώς ψηλά οι ουρανοί
κι εδώ στη γη τώρ' ας φανή,
κάθε πνοή να Σε αινή.

WORDS: Nahum Tate and Nicholas Brady
MUSIC: Thomas Tallis
Words all tr. © The Christian Science Board of Directors

TALLIS' CANON
L.M.
Alternate tunes: 1, 446, 447

Igbo

K'ebulie G'elu Chine-ke,
Dik'ebube Gi juru igwe,
K'egosi kwa ya etua n'uwa,
Rue mgbe'mere uche Gi ebea.

Iluko

O. Apo Diosmi iti natan-ok,
Ti gloriam punnuen na't law-ang;
Iti langit ken 'toy daga
Ti naganmo ita dayawen mi

Indonesian

Tuhan, bagiMu pujian,
LangitMu p'nuh kemuliaan,
Biar dunia ikut menyembah,
Pada hukumMu berserah.

Japanese

いと高き神よ
光　空にみち
この地にも満たし
み国を　われらに

Norwegian

Vær høyt opphøyet, Du, vår Gud,
Til himlen når Din herlighet,
Dens glans la skinne på oss ned,
Til Du blir adlydt her og nu.

Polish

„Bądź uwielbiony, Ojcze nasz!
Jak niebo chwali imię Twe,
Tak niech Ci ziemia składa hołd,
Aż Twoją wolę przyjmie świat."

Portuguese

Louvado sejas Tu, ó Deus!
Tua glória, ao encher os céus,
Reflita-se também aqui,
Em nossa obediência a Ti.

Russian

Возвысим, Господи, Тебя;
Твой блеск, наполнив небеса,
Пусть также будет на земле,
Когда все следуют Тебе.

Spanish

Enaltecido seas, Tú,
oh Dios de amor y de bondad;
henchido de Tu gloria está
el ancho y puro cielo azul.
Despliega pues, Señor, también
Tu gloria en suelo terrenal,
que sepa hoy y aquí el mortal
Tu santo imperio obedecer.

Swedish

Dig, Herre Gud, upphöja vi,
Din ära må förkunnad bli
– Såsom i himlen så på jord –
Tills alla lyda här Ditt ord!

446 Be Thou, O God

Communion Doxology

Be Thou, O God, ex - alt - ed high; And

as Thy glo - ry fills the sky, So let it be on

earth dis - played, Till Thou art here and now o - beyed.

WORDS: Nahum Tate and Nicholas Brady
MUSIC: Japanese melody; arr. CSPS

KI RI SU TO NO
L.M.
Alternate tunes: 1, 445, 447

Be Thou, O God

447

Communion Doxology

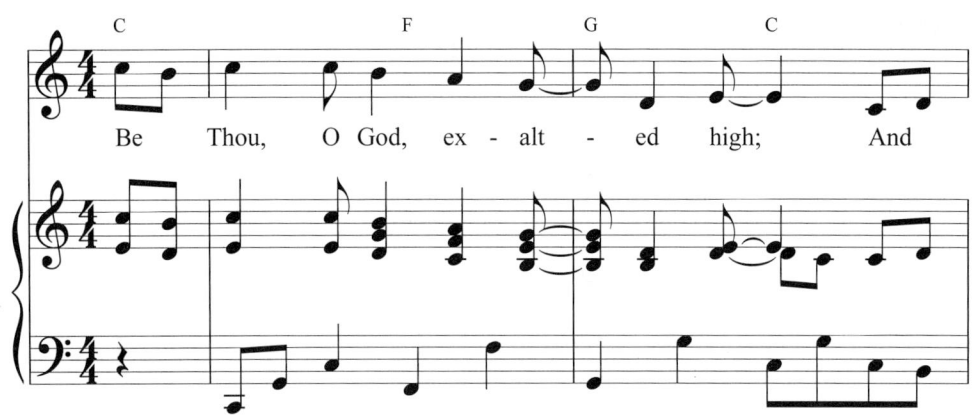

Be Thou, O God, ex - alt - ed high; And

as Thy glo - ry fills the sky, So let it be on earth

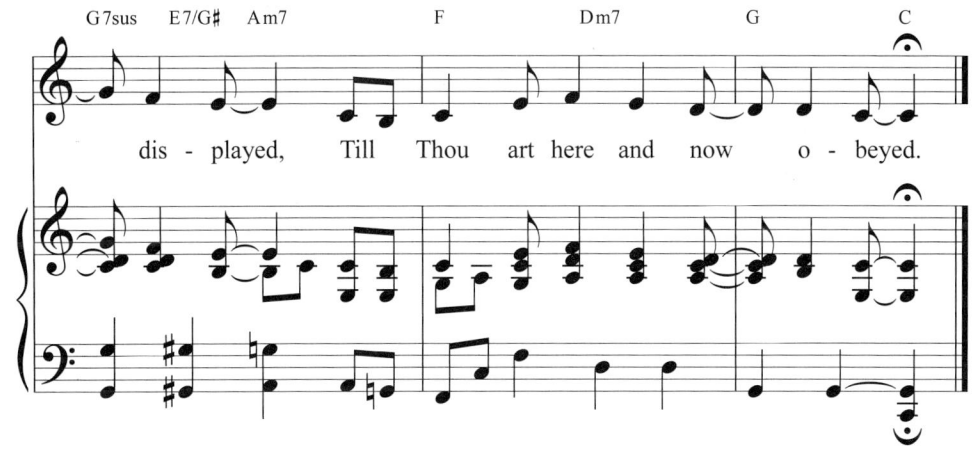

dis - played, Till Thou art here and now o - beyed.

WORDS: Nahum Tate and Nicholas Brady
MUSIC: Désirée Goyette

Music © 2017 The Christian Science Board of Directors

EXALTED
L.M.
Alternate tunes: 1, 445, 446

448   Bless the Lord, Oh My Soul

Psalms 103:1–4.

WORDS: Gene Rice and Charlene Moore Cooper
MUSIC: Gene Rice; harm. Charlene Moore Cooper, alt.; arr. CSPS

BLESS THE LORD
Irregular

Verses

1. And all that is with - in me, And
2. Who for - gives all your in - iq - ui - ties, Who for -
3. Who heals all your dis - eas - es, Who
4. Who crowns you with love and hon - or, Who

all that is with - in me, And all that is with -
gives all your in - iq - ui - ties, Who for - gives all your in -
heals all your dis - eas - es, Who heals all your dis -
crowns you with love and hon - or, Who crowns you with love and

to Refrain

in me, Bless God's ho - ly name!
iq - ui - ties, Bless God's ho - ly name!
eas - es, Bless God's ho - ly name!
hon - or, Bless God's ho - ly name!

449 Blest Christmas Morn

"Christmas Morn" by Mary Baker Eddy

1. Blest Christ-mas morn, though murk-y clouds Pur-sue thy way,

Thy light was born where storm en-shrouds Nor dawn nor day!

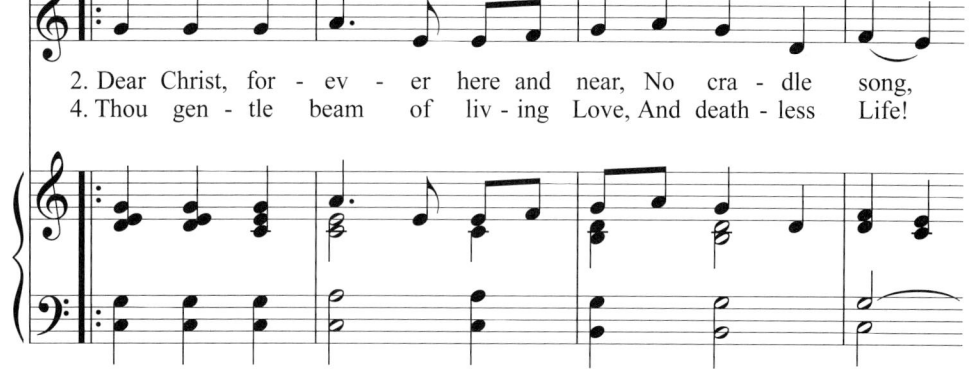

2. Dear Christ, for-ev-er here and near, No cra-dle song,
4. Thou gen-tle beam of liv-ing Love, And death-less Life!

WORDS: Mary Baker Eddy
MUSIC: Désirée Goyette
Music © 2014 The Christian Science Board of Directors

CLARITY
8.4.8.4.
Alternate tunes: 23–28, 450, 451

450 Blest Christmas Morn

"Christmas Morn" by Mary Baker Eddy

1. Blest Christ - mas morn, though murk - y clouds Pur -
3. Thou God - i - de - a, Life - en-crowned, The

sue thy way, Thy light was born where
Beth - lehem babe— Be - loved, re - plete, by

storm en-shrouds Nor dawn nor day! 2. Dear Christ, for - ev - er
flesh em-bound—Was but thy shade! 4. Thou gen - tle beam of

WORDS: Mary Baker Eddy
MUSIC: Fenella Bennetts
Music © 2008 The Christian Science Board of Directors

NEWBORN
8.4.8.4.
Alternate tunes: 23–28, 449, 451

451 Blest Christmas Morn

"Christmas Morn" by Mary Baker Eddy

1. Blest Christmas morn, though murk-y clouds Pur-sue thy way,
3. Thou God-i-de-a, Life-en-crowned, The Beth-lehem babe—
5. Or cru-el creed, or earth-born taint: Fill us to-day

end here

Thy light was born where storm en-shrouds Nor dawn nor day!
Be-loved, re-plete, by flesh em-bound—Was but thy shade!
With all thou art— be thou our saint, Our stay, al-way.

2. Dear Christ, for-ev-er here and near, No cra-dle song,
4. Thou gen-tle beam of liv-ing Love, And death-less Life!

to beginning

No na-tal hour and moth-er's tear, To thee be-long.
Truth in-fi-nite,— so far a-bove All mor-tal strife,

WORDS: Mary Baker Eddy
MUSIC: Robert Rockabrand
Music © 2008 The Christian Science Board of Directors

HODGSON
8.4.8.4.
Alternate tunes: 23–28, 449, 450

Brood O'er Us

452

"Love" by Mary Baker Eddy

1. Brood o'er us with Thy shel-t'ring wing, 'Neath which our spir-its
2. If thou the bend-ing reed wouldst break By thought or word un-
3. Learn, too, that wis-dom's rod is given For faith to kiss, and
4. Through God, who gave that word of might Which swelled cre-a-tion's
5. Thou to whose power our hope we give, Free us from hu-man

blend Like broth-er birds, that soar and sing, And
kind, Pray that his spir-it you par-take, Who
know; That greet-ings glo-rious from high heaven, Whence
lay: "Let there be light, and there was light." What
strife. Fed by Thy love di-vine we live, For

on the same branch bend. The ar-row that doth
loved and healed man-kind: Seek ho-ly thoughts and
joys su-per-nal flow, Come from that Love, di-
chased the clouds a-way? 'Twas Love whose fin-ger
Love a-lone is Life; And life most sweet, as

wound the dove Darts not from those who watch and love.
heaven-ly strain, That make men one in love re-main.
vine-ly near, Which chas-tens pride and earth-born fear,
traced a-loud A bow of prom-ise on the cloud.
heart to heart Speaks kind-ly when we meet and part.

WORDS: Mary Baker Eddy
MUSIC: James Leith Macbeth Bain; adapt. and harm. Robert Rockabrand
Music adapt. and harm. © 2008 The Christian Science Board of Directors

BROTHER JAMES' AIR
8.6.8.6.8.8.
Alternate tunes: 30–32, 453–456

453 Brood O'er Us

"Love" by Mary Baker Eddy

1. Brood o'er us with Thy shel-t'ring wing,
   'Neath which our spir - its blend
   Like broth - er birds, that soar and sing, And
2. If thou the bend - ing reed wouldst break
   By thought or word un - kind,
   Pray that his spir - it you par - take, Who
3. Learn, too, that wis - dom's rod is given
   For faith to kiss, and know;
   That greet - ings glo - rious from high heaven, Whence
4. Through God, who gave that word of might
   Which swelled cre - a - tion's lay:
   "Let there be light, and there was light." What
5. Thou to whose power our hope we give,
   Free us from hu - man strife.
   Fed by Thy love di - vine we live, For

WORDS: Mary Baker Eddy
MUSIC: Désirée Goyette
Music © 2016 The Christian Science Board of Directors

LILY
8.6.8.6.8.8.
Alternate tunes: 30–32, 452, 454–456

454 Brood O'er Us

"Love" by Mary Baker Eddy

1. Brood o'er us with Thy shel - t'ring wing,
2. If thou the bend - ing reed wouldst break
3. Learn, too, that wis - dom's rod is given
4. Through God, who gave that word of might
5. Thou to whose power our hope we give,

'Neath which our spir - its blend
By thought or word un - kind,
For faith to kiss, and know;
Which swelled cre - a - tion's lay:
Free us from hu - man strife.

Like broth - er birds, that soar and sing,
Pray that his spir - it you par - take,
That greet - ings glo - rious from high heaven,
"Let there be light, and there was light."
Fed by Thy love di - vine we live,

WORDS: Mary Baker Eddy
MUSIC: James R. Corbett
Music © 2017 The Christian Science Board of Directors

BROTHER BIRDS
8.6.8.6.8.8.
Alternate tunes: 30–32, 452, 453, 455, 456

Brood O'er Us

Oh, bajo Tu ala tutelar

"Love" by Mary Baker Eddy

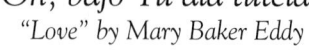

English
1. Brood o'er us with Thy shel-t'ring wing, 'Neath
2. If thou the bend-ing reed wouldst break By
3. Learn, too, that wis-dom's rod is given For

Spanish
1. Oh, ba-jo Tu a-la tu-te-lar se-
2. Si tu pa-la-bra_o ac-to cruel la
3. La va-ra del sa-ber ca-bal es

which our spir-its blend Like broth-er birds, that
thought or word un-kind, Pray that his spir-it
faith to kiss, and know; That greet-ings glo-rious

re-mos en el bien a-lon-dras que pa-
ca-ña des-tro-zó, pi-de_al Se-ñor el
don que da la fe, y_hay un men-sa-je

soar and sing, And on the same branch
you par-take, Who loved and healed man-
from high heaven, Whence joys su-per-nal

ra_a-ni-dar la mis-ma ra-ma
don de_a-quel que_al hom-bre_a-mó y sa-
ce-les-tial que_en glo-ria_y luz se

bend. The ar-row that doth wound the dove Darts
kind: Seek ho-ly thoughts and heaven-ly strain, That
flow, Come from that Love, di-vine-ly near, Which

ven. La fle-cha que nos da do-lor no
nó. Pro-cu-ra tú_en el bien pen-sar, que_a
ve. Lo man-da el cer-ca-no_A-mor que hu-

WORDS: Mary Baker Eddy; Sp. tr. CSPS
MUSIC: Melanie H. Alcázar; arr. CSPS

Sp. tr. © 1946, ren. 1974 The Christian Science Board of Directors
Music © 2016 The Christian Science Board of Directors

LOVE
8.6.8.6.8.8.
Alternate tunes: 30–32, 452–454, 456

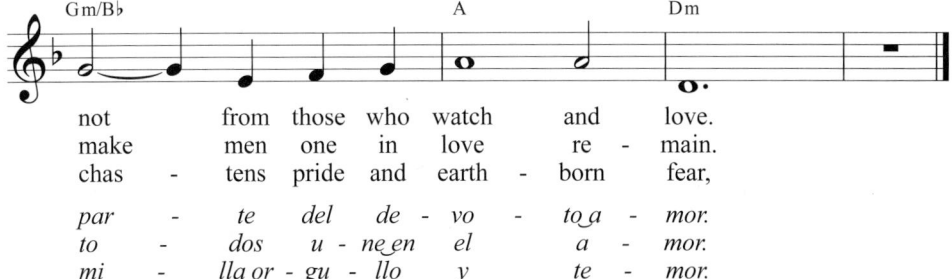

not		from	those	who	watch		and		love.
make		men	one	in	love		re	-	main.
chas	-	tens	pride	and	earth	-	born		fear,

par - *te* *del* *de* - *vo* - *to a* - *mor.*
to - *dos* *u* - *ne en* *el* *a* - *mor.*
mi - *lla or* - *gu* - *llo* *y* *te* - *mor.*

English

4. Through God, who gave that word of might
   Which swelled creation's lay:
   "Let there be light, and there was light."
   What chased the clouds away?
   'Twas Love whose finger traced aloud
   A bow of promise on the cloud.

5. Thou to whose power our hope we give,
   Free us from human strife.
   Fed by Thy love divine we live,
   For Love alone is Life;
   And life most sweet, as heart to heart
   Speaks kindly when we meet and part.

Spanish

4. *Dios hizo con Su voz nacer*
   de Sí la creación:
   "Sea la luz; y fue la luz."
   ¿Quién nubes disipó?
   Amor, que traza la feraz
   promesa en iris fiel de paz.

5. *Tú, que esperanza a todos das,*
   nos libras del rencor.
   Tu amor la vida es en verdad,
   pues Vida es sólo Amor;
   muy dulce vida si al hablar
   lo hacemos siempre con bondad.

456

Brood O'er Us

"Love" by Mary Baker Eddy

1. Brood o'er us with Thy shel-t'ring wing, 'Neath which our spir-its blend Like broth-er birds, that soar and sing, And on the same branch bend. The ar-row that doth wound the dove Darts not from those who watch and love.

2. If thou the bend-ing reed wouldst break By thought or word un-kind, Pray that his spir-it you par-take, Who loved and healed man-kind: Seek ho-ly thoughts and heaven-ly strain, That make men one in love re-main.

3. Learn, too, that wis-dom's rod is given For faith to kiss, and know; That greet-ings glo-rious from high heaven, Whence joys su-per-nal flow, Come from that Love, di-vine-ly near, Which chas-tens pride and earth-born fear,

WORDS: Mary Baker Eddy
MUSIC: Peter B. Allen
Music © 2008 The Christian Science Board of Directors

NOCTURNE
8.6.8.6.8.8.
Alternate tunes: 30–32, 452–455

4. Through God, who gave that word of might Which swelled cre-
a - tion's lay: "Let there be light, and there was light."
What chased the clouds a - way? 'Twas Love whose fin - ger
traced a - loud A bow of prom - ise on the cloud.

5. Thou to whose power our hope we give, Free us from hu-man strife.
Fed by Thy love di - vine we live, For Love a -
lone is Life; And life most sweet, as heart to heart
Speaks kind - ly when we meet and part.

457 Cause Me to Hear

Refrain

Cause me to hear Your lov-ing-kind-ness in the morn-ing;

Teach me to do Your will, O God.

Cause me to know the way where I should place my feet To

WORDS: Para. I Kings 19:11, 12, Psalms 23:2, 4, Psalms 143:8, 10 Susan Thierman
MUSIC: Susan Thierman

IN THE STILLNESS
Irregular

458 Christ Comes, with Succor Speedy

1. Christ comes, with suc - cor speed - y, To those who suf - fer wrong;
2. God's bless - ings come as show - ers Up - on the thirst - y earth;
3. To God shall prayer un - ceas - ing, And dai - ly vows, as - cend;

To help the poor and need - y, And bid the weak be strong;
And joy and hope, like flow - ers, Spring in His path to birth.
Love's king-dom still in - creas - ing, A king-dom with - out end.

Christ comes to break op - pres - sion, To set the cap - tive free,
Be - fore Him on the moun - tains Shall Peace, the her - ald, go;
The tide of time shall nev - er God's cov - e - nant re - move;

To take a - way trans - gres - sion, And rule in eq - ui - ty.
From hill to vale the foun - tains Of right - eous-ness shall flow.
Her name shall stand for - ev - er: Her change-less name of Love.

Isaiah 52:7; 54:10 / Ezekiel 34:26. The music of this hymn is based on a German folk melody first published in the early 17th century.

WORDS: James Montgomery, adapt.
MUSIC: German melody; harm. George Ratcliffe Woodward, alt.
Words adapt. © 1932, ren. 1960 The Christian Science Board of Directors

ES FLOG EIN KLEINS WALDVÖGELEIN
7.6.7.6.D.
Alternate tune: 75

Come, Gracious Spirit

459

1. Come, gra - cious Spir - it, heaven - ly Love,
2. The light of Truth to us dis - play,

With light and com - fort from a - bove;
That we may know and choose Your way;

Be Truth our guard - ian, Love our guide, O'er
Plant ho - ly joy in ev - ery heart, That

ev - ery thought and step pre - side, Be God our guide.
we from You may ne'er de -

part, Plant joy in ev - ery heart.

3. Lead us, O Christ, the liv - ing Way, Nor let us from your pre - cepts

stray; Lead us to God, our heaven - ly rest, That

we may be for - ev - er blest, For - ev - er blest.

WORDS: Simon Browne, adapt., alt.
MUSIC: Andrew D. Brewis

ORCHARDS
L.M.
Alternate tune: 39

460 Come, O Fount of Every Blessing

1. Come, O fount of ev-ery bless-ing, Tune our hearts to sing Your grace.
2. Come, O fount of ev-ery vi-sion, Lift our eyes to what will come.
3. Come, O fount of in-spi-ra-tion, Turn our lives to high-er ways.

Streams of mer-cy nev-er ceas-ing, Call for songs of deep-est praise.
See the li-on and the young lamb Dwell to-geth-er in Your home.
Lift our gloom and des-per-a-tion, Show the prom-ise of this day.

While the truth of life's per-fec-tion Fills our hearts with joy and love,
Hear the cries of war fall si-lent, Feel our love glow like the sun.
Help us bind our-selves in un-ion, Help our hands tell of our love.

Teach us ev-er to be faith-ful, May we still Your good-ness prove.
When we all serve one an-oth-er, Then our heav-en is be-gun.
With Your grace, O fount of jus-tice, Earth be fair as heaven a-bove.

Isaiah 11:6.

WORDS: Verse 1 Robert Robinson, adapt., alt.; verses 2, 3 Eugene B. Navias, alt.
MUSIC: American melody, Wyeth's *Repository of Sacred Music, Part Second*, 1813
Words vss. 2–3 © 1991 Eugene B. Navias

NETTLETON
8.7.8.7.D.

Come unto Me

461

1. Come un-to me, you wea-ry, And I will give you rest.
These ten-der words of Je-sus Still come to hearts op-pressed.
They tell of be-ne-dic-tion, Of par-don, grace, and peace,
Of joy that has no end-ing, Of love that can-not cease.

2. Come un-to me, you wan-derers, And I will give you light.
These lov-ing words of Je-sus Still come to cheer the night.
Come, all you heav-y lad-en, And I will give you life.
These peace-ful words of Je-sus Still come to end all strife.

Matthew 11:28. Generally described as a Scottish folk song, authorship of this melody was claimed by Lady John Douglas Scott (née Alicia Ann Spottiswoode), who also altered the poem ("Annie Laurie," by William Douglas) with which it was originally paired.

WORDS: William Chatterton Dix, adapt., alt.
MUSIC: Scottish melody; harm. CSPS

ANNIE LAURIE
7.6.7.6.D.
Alternate tune: 43

462   Come, You Disconsolate

1. Come, you dis-con-so-late, wher-e'er you lan-guish,
2. Joy of the des-o-late, light of the stray-ing,
3. Here see the Bread of Life, see wat-ers flow-ing

Here health and peace are found, Life, Truth, and Love;
Hope of the pen-i-tent, fade-less and pure;
Forth from the throne of God, pure from a-bove;

Here bring your wound-ed hearts, here tell your an-guish;
Here speaks the Com-fort-er, ten-der-ly say-ing,
Come to the feast of love, come, ev-er know-ing,

Earth has no sor-row but Love can re-move.
Earth has no sor-row that Love can-not cure.
Earth has no sor-row but Love can re-move.

John 6:35, 48, 51 / Revelation 22:1.

WORDS: Verses 1, 2 Thomas Moore, adapt., alt.; verse 3 Thomas Hastings, adapt.
MUSIC: A. Fritsch, adapt.; harm. *Liederbuch der Christlichen Wissenschaft*, 1924

11.10.11.10.
Alternate tune: 40

Day by Day the Manna Fell

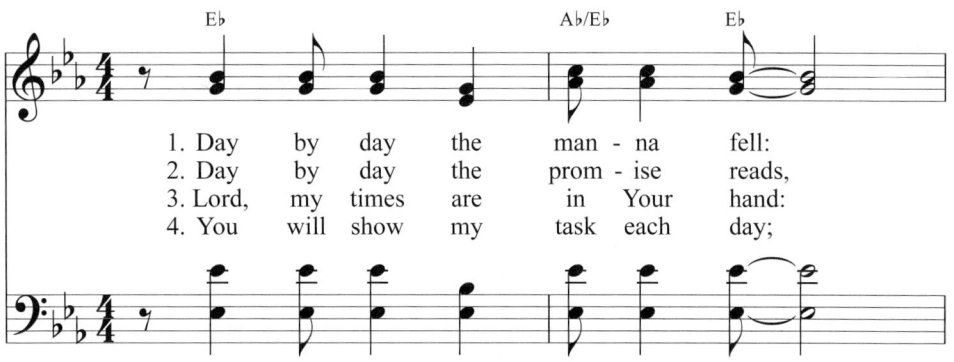

1. Day by day the man-na fell:
2. Day by day the prom-ise reads,
3. Lord, my times are in Your hand:
4. You will show my task each day;

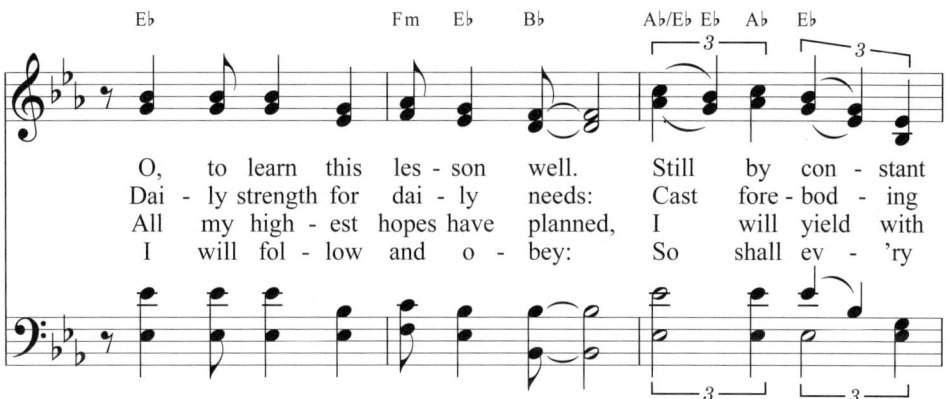

O, to learn this les-son well. Still by con - stant
Dai - ly strength for dai - ly needs: Cast fore - bod - ing
All my high - est hopes have planned, I will yield with
I will fol - low and o - bey: So shall ev - 'ry

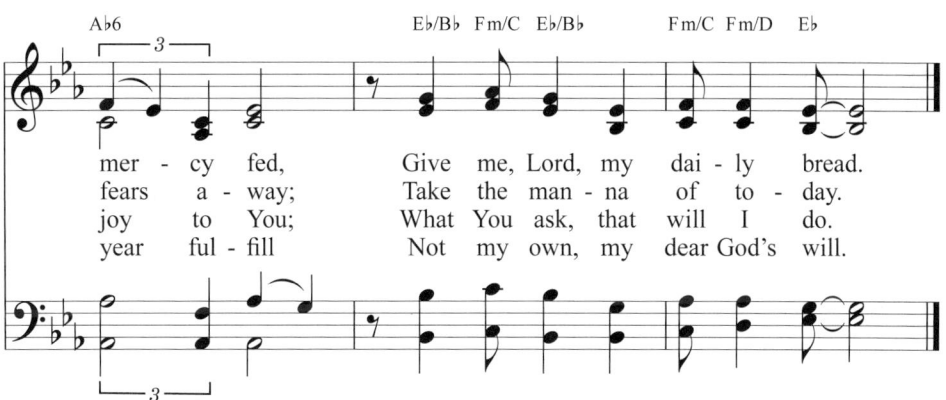

mer - cy fed, Give me, Lord, my dai - ly bread.
fears a - way; Take the man - na of to - day.
joy to You; What You ask, that will I do.
year ful - fill Not my own, my dear God's will.

Exodus 16:15 / Deuteronomy 8:13. This music originates with the Yoruba people, a large African ethnic group mainly located in Nigeria and Benin, but with populations in several coastal countries ranging as far west as Sierra Leone.

WORDS: Josiah Conder, alt.
MUSIC: Yoruba melody; arr. Emmanuel Badejo
Music arr. © Emmanuel Badejo

7.7.7.7.
Alternate tunes: 46, 47

464 Dear Master, May I Follow Thee

1. Dear Mas - ter, may I fol - low thee With ho - ly, deep sin-
2. Lead me to wor - ship God a - right, In truth, in spir - it,

cer - i - ty, Form - ing each thought to Christ - ly mold,
seek the light; Lov - ing pure good with heart and soul,

Feel - ing your peace my heart en - fold.
Lov - ing each neigh - bor, per - fect, whole.

3. May I per - ceive all be - ing one, Per - fect Fa - ther,

WORDS: W. Brian Cork
MUSIC: W. Brian Cork; arr. CSPS

ARNISDALE
L.M.

per - fect son; Let me hold fast this heaven-ly view,

Find - ing each day my life made new.

4. May I see mor - tal self dis - solve, Take up the cross with

firm re - solve, Seek - ing the vic - tor's crown each day,

Hum - ble and lov - ing all the way.

465 Dear Shepherd, You Are Love Divine

1. Dear Shep-herd, You are Love di-vine, You meet my ev-ery need.
4. Your good-ness spreads be-fore my eyes; No en-e-my You know.

Where fields are green and wa-ters still I rest, I drink, I feed.
Your oil is poured up-on my head; My cup, it o-ver-flows.

2. Your love re-stores my thirst-y soul, And leads me from the wild
5. Your grace and mer-cy ev-ery day Bring bless-ings from a-bove.

Psalm 23.

WORDS and MUSIC: Fenella Bennetts
Words and Music © 2017 The Christian Science Board of Directors

GREENFIELD
Irregular

end here

To walk in ways of Truth and Life As Your be-lov-ed child.
I'm liv-ing in the house of God, The con-scious-ness of Love.

3. And e-ven when the shade of death Sug-gests that we can part,

No fear of e-vil en-ters here; Your strength and guid-ance,

to beginning

ev-er near, Bring com-fort to my heart.

466   Dear Lord, Lead Me, Day by Day

1. Dear Lord, lead me, day by day; Make me ho - ly, strong and wise.
2. Dear Lord, lead me, day by day; Your great love will end all strife.
3. Now, with thank - ful trust, I sing Joy - ous prais - es to one God,

Hap - py, most of all, to say, All are per - fect in Your eyes.
Make me fol - low and o - bey Faith - ful - ly the Word of Life.
And from up - right hearts will spring Deeds of love, here and a - broad.

Refrain

Praise to God, fount of love, Praise from morn 'til the new day's birth;

Praise in church, praise at home, Praise to God ev - 'ry - where on earth.

Psalm 61.

WORDS: Francisca Asuncion, alt.
MUSIC: Filipino melody; harm. Francisca Asuncion
Words and Music arr. © 1983 The United Methodist Publishing House (admin. Music Services)

COTTAGE GROVE
7.7.7.7.Ref.

Eternal Mind the Potter Is

467

1. E - ter - nal Mind the Pot - ter is, And thought th'e - ter - nal clay:
2. God could not make im - per - fect man His mod - el in - fi - nite;

The hand that fash - ions is di - vine, His works pass not a - way.
Un - hal - lowed thought He could not plan, Love's work and Love must fit.

Man is the no - blest work of God, His beau - ty, power and grace,
Life, Truth and Love the pat - tern make, Christ is the per - fect heir;

Im - mor - tal; per - fect as his Mind Re - flect - ed face to face.
The clouds of sense roll back, and show The form di - vine - ly fair.

3. God's will is done; His king - dom come; The Pot - ter's work is plain.

The long - ing to be good and true Has brought the light a - gain.

And man does stand as God's own child, The im - age of His love.

Let glad - ness ring from ev - ery tongue, And heaven and earth ap - prove.

Matthew 6:10 / Luke 11:2 / Romans 8:17.

WORDS: Mary Alice Dayton
MUSIC: Andrew D. Brewis
Music © 2011 Andrew D. Brewis

FRIEND
C.M.D.
Alternate tunes: 51, 52, 468

468 Eternal Mind the Potter Is

1. E - ter - nal Mind the Pot - ter is, And thought th'e - ter - nal clay: The hand that fash - ions is di - vine, His works pass not a - way. Man is the no - blest

(2.) could not make im - per - fect man His mod - el in - fi - nite; Un - hal - lowed thought He could not plan, Love's work and Love must fit. Life, Truth and Love the

(3.) will is done; His king - dom come; The Pot - ter's work is plain. The long - ing to be good and true Has brought the light a - gain. And man does stand as

Matthew 6:10 / Luke 11:2 / Romans 8:17.

WORDS: Mary Alice Dayton
MUSIC: Cherie Brennan
Music © 2016 The Christian Science Board of Directors

CONSCIOUSNESS
C.M.D.
Alternate tunes: 51, 52, 467

469 Eternal God, the Cause of All Creation

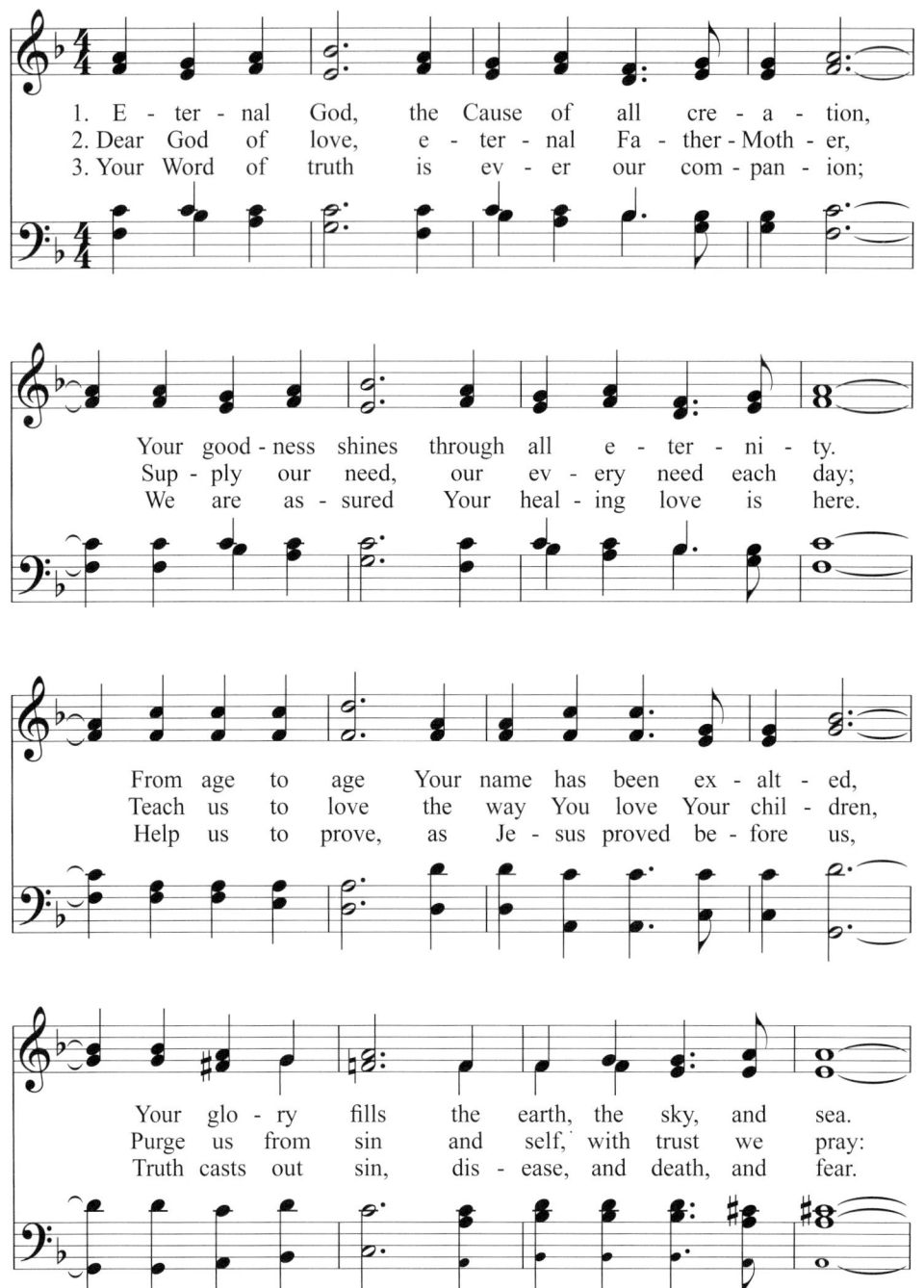

1. E - ter - nal God, the Cause of all cre - a - tion,
2. Dear God of love, e - ter - nal Fa - ther-Moth - er,
3. Your Word of truth is ev - er our com - pan - ion;

Your good - ness shines through all e - ter - ni - ty.
Sup - ply our need, our ev - ery need each day;
We are as - sured Your heal - ing love is here.

From age to age Your name has been ex - alt - ed,
Teach us to love the way You love Your chil - dren,
Help us to prove, as Je - sus proved be - fore us,

Your glo - ry fills the earth, the sky, and sea.
Purge us from sin and self, with trust we pray:
Truth casts out sin, dis - ease, and death, and fear.

Matthew 6:10 / Luke 11:2. The music of this hymn is arranged from *Finlandia*, a symphonic work by Finnish composer Jean Sibelius written in 1900. Widely considered to be Finland's finest composer, Sibelius was highly prolific, contributing most substantially in both choral and orchestral genres.

WORDS: Oak E. Davis, adapt.
MUSIC: Jean Sibelius; transc. CSPS
Words © 1948, ren. 1976 Carl Fischer, Inc.

FINLANDIA
11.10.11.10.11.10.
Alternate arr: 561

Al - might - y One, cre - a - tive Mind, our Mak - er,
"Thy king - dom come," in all earth as in heav - en,
And may Your Word a - bide with us for - ev - er,

Which was, and is, and ev - er - more shall be.
You are our light, our guide, our hope, our stay.
O Lord of life, of truth, and love, most dear.

470 Faith Grasps the Blessing

1. Faith grasps the bless - ing she de - sires, Hope points the up - ward gaze; And Love, ce - les - tial Love, in - spires The el - o - quence of praise.

2. But sweet - er far the still small voice Un - heard by hu - man ear, When God has made the heart re - joice, And dried the bit - ter tear.

3. No ac - cents flow, no words as - cend; All lan - guage fails us there; But God does al - ways com - pre - hend And an - swer si - lent prayer.

WORDS: Harriet Martineau, alt.
MUSIC: Peter B. Cornell
Music © 2017 The Christian Science Board of Directors

SHADOW RIDGE
C.M.
Alternate tune: 54

Father, Hear the Prayer We Offer   471

1. Fa - ther, hear the prayer we of - fer;
2. Not for - ev - er in green pas - tures
3. Not for - ev - er by still wa - ters

Not for ease that prayer shall be,
Do we ask our way to be,
Would we id - ly qui - et stay,

But for strength, that we may ev - er
But the steep and rug - ged path - way
But would smite the liv - ing foun - tains

Live our lives cou - ra - geous - ly.
May we tread re - joic - ing - ly.
From the rocks a - long our way.

WORDS: Love M. Willis
MUSIC: Russian melody; harm. Susan G. Wente, alt.
Music harm. © 1977 World Library Publications

8.7.8.7.
Alternate tune: 55

472 Father, You Are Very Near Us

1. Fa - ther, You are ver - y near us, Well we know that You will hear us, And will an - swer when we call, And will an - swer when we call: May the
2. Christ, the way of our sal - va - tion, Lifts the veil of sep - a - ra - tion, Shows our life in Spir - it, free, Shows our life in Spir - it, free— Shows the
3. Fa - ther, this most won - drous un - ion We would prove in blessed com - mu - nion: Take the Truth, our bread from heaven, Take the Truth, our bread from heaven, Drink the

Psalms 86:6–7. These words are from a poem first published in 1935 as a solo with music by Percy Buck.

WORDS: Violet Hay, alt.
MUSIC: Désirée Goyette
BENJAMIN
8.8.7.7.8.8.9.9.

473 Father-Mother God
Père-Mère Dieu

English
1. Fa - ther - Moth - er God, All - in - all, Re - as -
2. You will guide me by day and night. I go
3. Now I find, as nev - er be - fore, I'm de -

French
1. Pè - re - Mè - re Dieu, Tout - en - tout Sur la
2. Tu me gui - des jour et nuit. Je Te
3. Main - te - nant plus que ja - mais, Dé - vou -

sur - ing me ev - ery day, You en - cour - age
forth with no doubt or fear, For I feel Your
vot - ed to serv - ing You, Your pure good - ness

rou - te Tu me ras - su - res, Pour tou - jours de
suis sans peur ni dou - te. Où pour - rais-je trou -
é à Te ser - vir, Je prends part

me on my way. Fa - ther - Moth - er God, All - in - all.
love with me here, Fa - ther - Moth - er God, All - in - all.
fills me a - new, Fa - ther - Moth - er God, All - in - all.

Ton grand a - mour; Pè - re - Mè - re Dieu, Tout - en - tout.
ver plus d'a - mour; Pè - re - Mè - re Dieu, Tout - en - tout ?
à Ta bon - té Pè - re - Mè - re Dieu, Tout - en - tout.

This hymn, from Cameroon, was inspired by Mary Baker Eddy's comprehensive concept of God as Father-Mother.

WORDS: Honla Honla Joseph; Eng. tr. CSPS
MUSIC: Honla Honla Joseph; transc. and arr. CSPS
Fr. Words, Eng. tr., Music © 2016 The Christian Science Board of Directors

PRIERE D'ENFANT
8.8.8.8.Ref.

474 Father, We Your Loving Children

1. Fa-ther, we Your lov-ing chil-dren Lift our hearts in joy to-day,
2. Come we dai-ly then, dear Fa-ther, O-pen hearts and will-ing hands,
3. In Your house se-cure-ly dwell-ing, Where Your chil-dren live to bless,
4. Fa-ther, we Your lov-ing chil-dren Lift our hearts in joy to-day,

end here

Know-ing well that You will keep us Ev-er in Your bless-ed way.
Ea-ger ears, ex-pec-tant, joy-ful, Read-y for Your right com-mands.
See-ing on-ly Your cre-a-tion, We can share Your hap-pi-ness,
Know-ing well that You will keep us Ev-er in Your bless-ed way.

You are Love and You are wis-dom, You are Life and You are All;
We would hear no oth-er voic-es, We would heed no oth-er call;
Share Your joy and spend it free-ly. Loy-al hearts can feel no fear;

to beginning

In Your Spir-it liv-ing, mov-ing, We shall nei-ther faint nor fall.
You a-lone are good and gra-cious, You our Mind and You our All.
We Your chil-dren know You, Fa-ther, Love and Life for-ev-er near.

WORDS: Elizabeth C. Adams, alt.
MUSIC: Joy Tessman and Scott Martin; transc. Robert Wyckoff, alt.

8.7.8.7.D.
Alternate tune: 58

Forget Not Who You Are

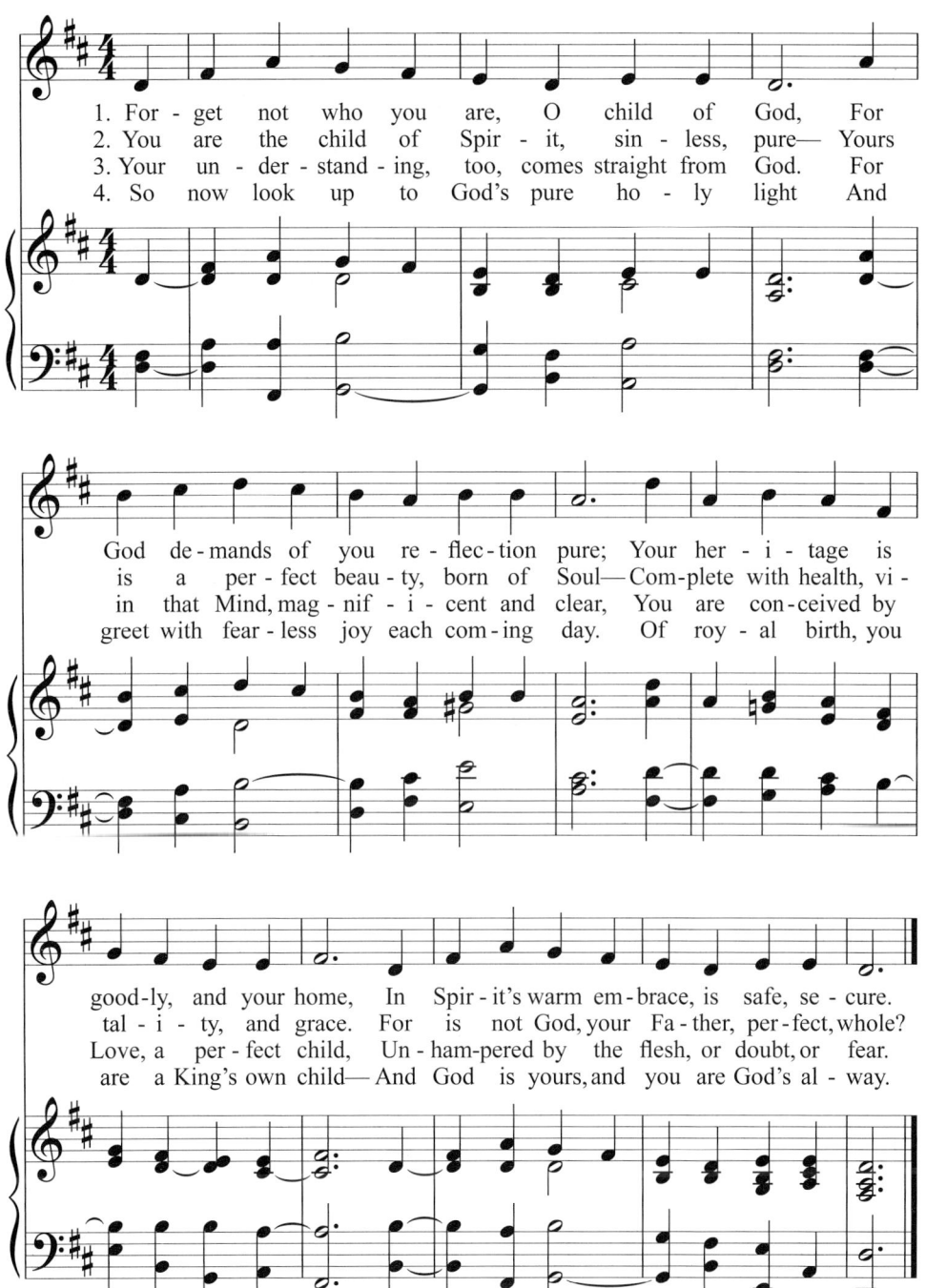

1. For-get not who you are, O child of God, For God de-mands of you re-flec-tion pure; Your her-i-tage is good-ly, and your home, In Spir-it's warm em-brace, is safe, se-cure.

2. You are the child of Spir-it, sin-less, pure— Yours is a per-fect beau-ty, born of Soul—Com-plete with health, vi-tal-i-ty, and grace. For is not God, your Fa-ther, per-fect, whole?

3. Your un-der-stand-ing, too, comes straight from God. For in that Mind, mag-nif-i-cent and clear, You are con-ceived by Love, a per-fect child, Un-ham-pered by the flesh, or doubt, or fear.

4. So now look up to God's pure ho-ly light And greet with fear-less joy each com-ing day. Of roy-al birth, you are a King's own child—And God is yours, and you are God's al-way.

Psalms 16:6. The words of this hymn are from a poem entitled "Thy Birthright," first printed in the September 1926 issue of *The Christian Science Journal.*

WORDS: Mildred Spring Case, alt.
MUSIC: Alfred Morton Smith

SURSUM CORDA
10.10.10.10.

Words alt. © 2017 The Christian Science Board of Directors
Music © 1941 Historic Church of the Ascension, Atlantic City, NJ (Admin. Episcopal Diocese of New Jersey)

476 Fearful Heart, Put All Your Cares

Banges Herz, leg deine Sorge

English
1. Fear-ful heart, put all your cares Com-plete-ly in your
2. Long-ing heart, don't give up hope When threats of e-vil

German
1. Ban-ges Herz, leg dei-ne Sor-ge ganz in dei-nes
2. Ban-ges Herz, ver-za-ge nicht, wenn des Irr-tums Macht dich

dear God's hands; Love feeds you with Her great strength
o-ver-whelm. Love now keeps Her prom-ise true,

GOT-TES Schoß, dass Er dich mit Kraft ver-sor-ge
schre-cket. Sieh, GOTT hält, was Er ver-spricht.

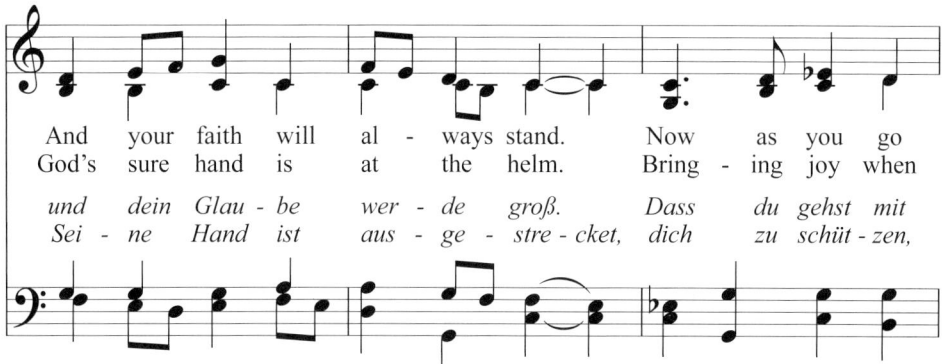

And your faith will al-ways stand. Now as you go
God's sure hand is at the helm. Bring-ing joy when

und dein Glau-be wer-de groß. Dass du gehst mit
Sei-ne Hand ist aus-ge-stre-cket, dich zu schüt-zen,

Isaiah 35:4.

WORDS: Friedrich Preller; Eng. tr. CSPS
MUSIC: Werner Kuck, alt.

SEI GETROST
7.8.7.7.8.7.8.7.

Ger. Words and Eng. tr. © 2017 The Christian Science Board of Directors

safe - ly for - ward, Walk se - cure - ly in Love's grace.
all seems dark - ness— God will keep you safe, se - cure.

si - chern Schrit - ten in der Kraft des Herrn ein - her,
dich zu lei - ten froh durch al - le Fin - ster - nis.

Give to God the praise and glo - ry; Fear and doubt have no more place.
You go for - ward, loved and peace - ful: Vic - to - ry is al - ways sure.

und du GOTT al - lein in - mit - ten Furcht und Zit - tern gibst die Ehr'!
Dei - nen Fuß lässt Er nicht glei - ten, und Sein Sieg, der ist ge - wiss!

477 Feed My Lambs, Tend My Sheep

Refrain

Feed my lambs, tend my sheep, O - ver all a vig - il keep;

In my name lead them forth Gent - ly as a shep - herd.

Verses

1. When they wan - der, when they stray, Their pro - tec - tor be.
2. Un - to all who lose the way, Hope and com - fort be.

John 21:15–17.

WORDS and MUSIC: Natalie Sleeth

Words and Music © 1972 Carl Fischer, Inc.

7.5.7.5.Ref.

As ye do un-to my flock, Thus ye do to me.
As ye do un-to my flock, Thus ye do to me. *to Refrain (altered)*

Refrain (altered)

Feed my lambs, tend my sheep, O-ver all a vig-il keep;

In my name lead them forth Gent - ly, gent - ly

as a lov-ing Shep-herd of the Lord.

478 From These Your Children

1. From these Your chil - dren gath - ered in Your name, From
2. O per - fect Life, in Your com - plete - ness held, None
3. O per - fect Mind, re - veal Your like - ness true, That
4. O Soul, in - spir - ing— give us vi - sion clear, Break

hearts made whole, from lips re - deemed from woe,
can be - yond Your om - ni - pres - ence stray;
high - er self - hood which we all must prove,
earth - bound fet - ters, sweep a - way the veil,

Your praise, Al - might - y, shall for - ev - er flow.
Safe in Your Love, we live and sing al - way,
Joy and do - min - ion, love re - flect - ing Love.
Show the new heaven and earth that shall pre - vail.

WORDS: Violet Hay, alt.
MUSIC: Andrew Sentinella

OXTED
10.10.10.10.Alleluias
Alternate tunes: 66, 421

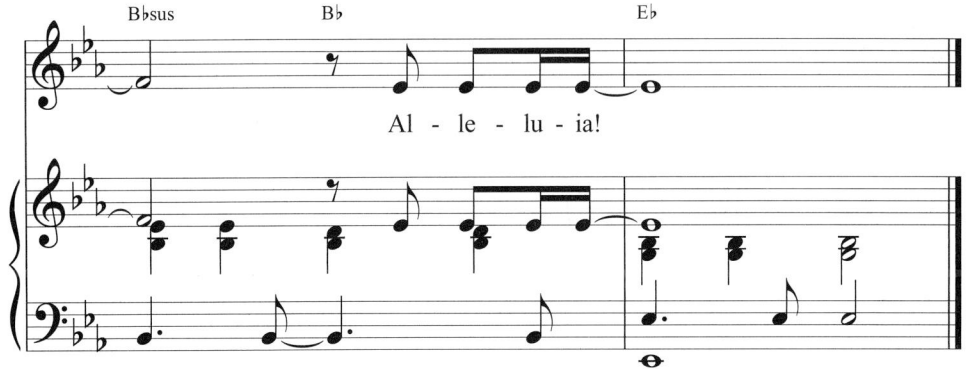

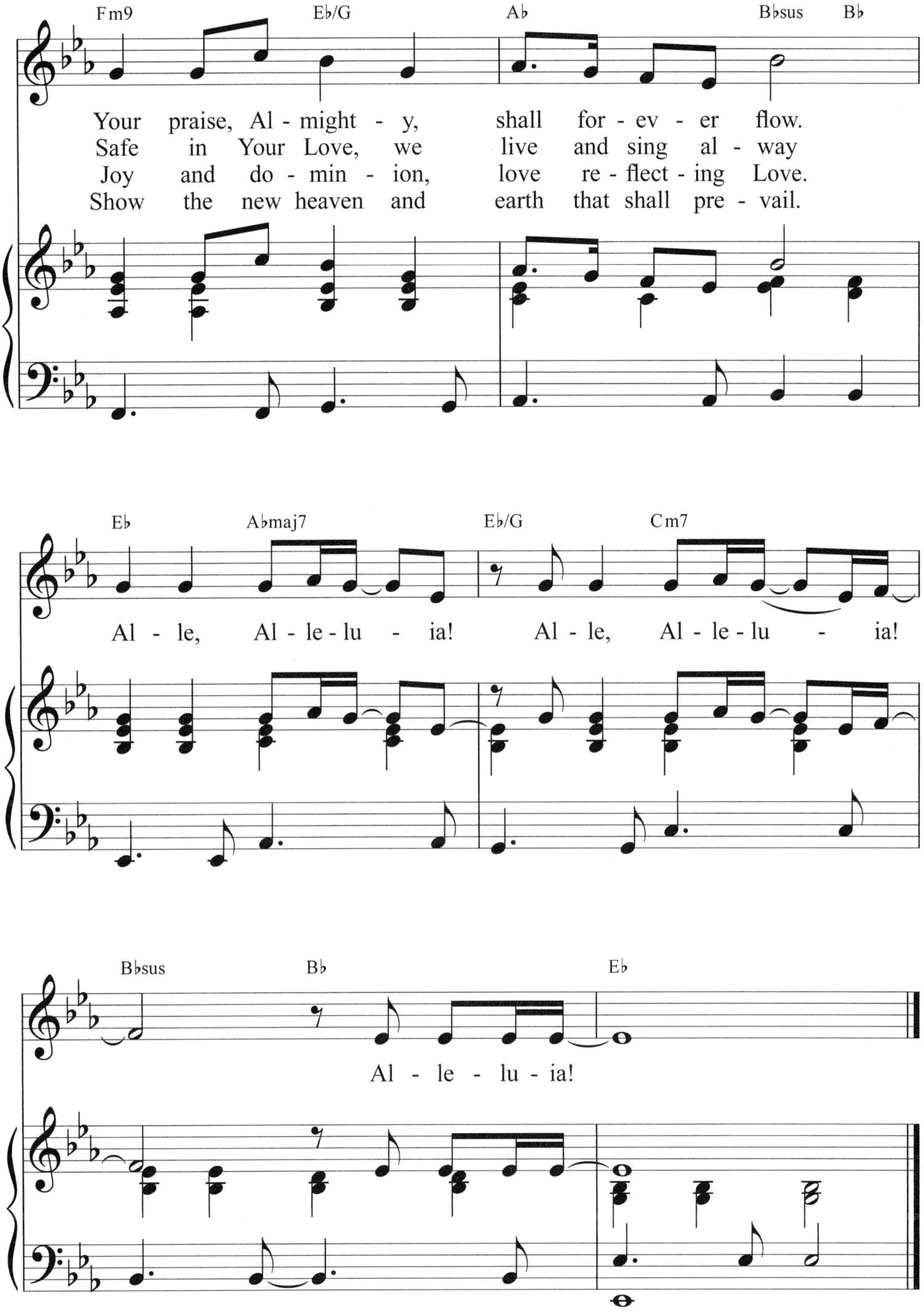

Fm9
Eb/G
Ab
Bbsus
Bb
Your praise, Al - might - y, shall for - ev - er flow.
Safe in Your Love, we live and sing al - way
Joy and do - min - ion, love re - flect - ing Love.
Show the new heaven and earth that shall pre - vail.
Eb
Abmaj7
Eb/G
Cm7
Al - le, Al - le - lu - ia! Al - le, Al - le - lu - ia!
Bbsus
Bb
Eb
Al - le - lu - ia!

479 Glorious Things of You Are Spoken

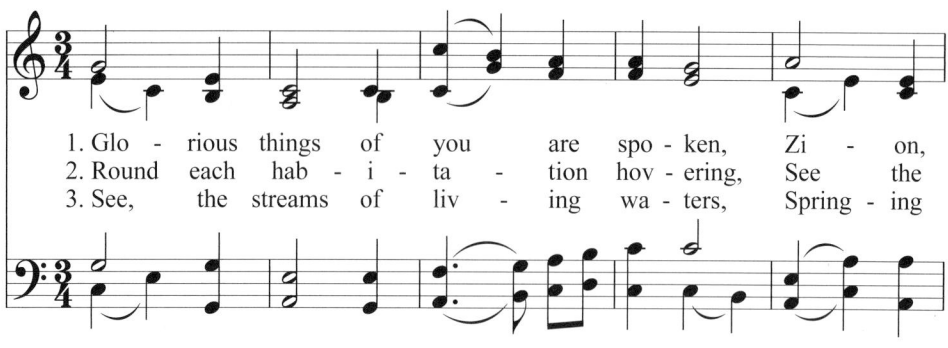

1. Glo - rious things of you are spo - ken, Zi - on,
2. Round each hab - i - ta - tion hov - ering, See the
3. See, the streams of liv - ing wa - ters, Spring - ing

cit - y of our God; Truth, whose word can -
cloud and fire ap - pear For a glo - ry
from e - ter - nal Love, Well sup - ply your

not be bro - ken, Formed you for its own a - bode:
and a cov - ering, Show - ing that the Lord is near.
sons and daugh - ters, And all fear of want re - move.

Exodus 13:21; 16:4, 15; 17:6 / Nehemiah 9:12, 15, 19, 20 / Psalms 78:14, 16, 24 / John 4:10. The words of this hymn are by John Newton, who also wrote the text to "Amazing Grace." Traditionally linked to a tune by Newton contemporary Austrian Franz Joseph Haydn, this music by Cyril V. Taylor was composed in May 1941 as a distinctly British alternative.

WORDS: John Newton, alt.
MUSIC: Cyril V. Taylor
Music © 1942. ren. 1970 Hope Publishing Company

ABBOT'S LEIGH
8.7.8.7.D.
Alternate tune: 71

On the Rock of A - ges found - ed, What can
Thus de - riv - ing from their ban - ner, Light by
None can faint, while such a riv - er Ev - er

shake your sure re - pose? By sal - va - tion's
night, and shade by day, Safe they feed up -
shall their thirst as - suage. Grace, which like the

walls sur - round - ed, You may smile at all your foes.
on the man - na, Which God gives them while they pray.
Lord, the giv - er, Nev - er fails from age to age.

480   Glory Be to God on High

1. Glo - ry be to God on high,
God whose glo - ry fills the sky;
Peace on earth to man is given,
Man, the well - be - loved of heaven.

2. Mark the won - ders of God's hand:
Power no em - pire can with - stand;
Wis - dom, an - gels' glo - rious theme;
Good - ness one e - ter - nal stream.

This music is based on a traditional Chinese melody. In addition to the arrangement given here, the hymn can be performed a capella, or with instruments doubling the melody line.

WORDS: Verse 1, lines 1-4 Charles Wesley; verse 1, lines 5-8 and verse 2 John Taylor, adapt.
MUSIC: Chinese melody; arr. CSPS

7.7.7.7.D.
Alternate tune: 72, 405

Fa - ther - Moth - er, in Your love, Send Your bless - ings
Let all peo - ple raise the song, End - less thanks to

from a - bove; Let Your light, Your truth, Your peace
God be - long; Hearts o'er - flow - ing with Love's praise

Bid all strife and tu - mult cease.
Join the hymns your voic - es raise.

481 Go to the World

1. Go to the world! Go in-to ev-ery place!
2. Go to the world! Go com-fort, bless, and pray.
3. Go to the world! Go as the ones I send,

Go live the word of God's re-deem-ing grace;
The nights of tears give way to joy-ful day.
For I am with you till the a-ges end,

Go seek God's pres-ence in each time and space.
In serv-ing God, we fol-low Christ's own way.
When all the hosts of glo-ry cry, "A-men!"

Matthew 28:19, 20 / Mark 16:15.

WORDS: Sylvia Dunstan, adapt.
MUSIC: Charles Villiers Stanford
Words © 1991 GIA Publications, Inc.

ENGELBERG
10.10.10.Alleluia

Al – le – lu – ia!   Al – le – lu – ia!

482 God Created Us in His Own Image

Deus criou o homem de Si mesmo

English
1. God cre - at - ed us in His own im - age,
2. Ev - ery - thing our Mas - ter Je - sus taught us

Portuguese
1. Deus cri - ou o ho - mem de Si mes - mo,
2. Tu - do o que Je - sus nos en - si - nou,

All the u - ni - verse is His cre - a - tion too;
Showed the way to love each oth - er dear - ly,

To - do o u - ni - ver - so E - le cri - ou tam - bém.
Foi a - mar os nos - sos se - me - lhan - tes.

He cre - at - ed us as His re - flec - tion,
When he healed the sick and freed the sin - ner,

Fez o ho - mem se - me - lhan - te a E - le,
E por ver as - sim tão bem o ho - mem

Fill - ing us with wis - dom, bold and true.
See - ing them in God's own light so clear - ly.

De sa - be - do - ri - a nos do - tou
E - le cu - ra - va os do - en - tes.

Life is made for liv - ing to the full - est,
As we gain the per - fect un - der - stand - ing

Pra vi - ver a vi - da ple - na - men - te
Quan - do to - dos nós com - pre - en - de - mos

Spir - it made us know - ing who we tru - ly are,
That e - ter - nal Mind is the All - in - all,

E sa - ber quem re - al - men - te so - mos.
Que só e - xis - te u - ma Men - te,

Irregular

WORDS: Graça de Maria Amorim dos Santos; Eng. tr. CSPS
MUSIC: Graça de Maria Amorim dos Santos; arr. CSPS

Dm ... G

Know-ing how to see re - al - i - ty, Pure and in - no -
We shall come to see re - al - i - ty, Pure and in - no -

Ve - mos a re - a - li - da - de, Pu - ra, i - no -
Ve - mos a re - a - li - da - de, Pu - ra, i - no -

G ... C C7

cent and free, Made in the like - ness of our God.
cent and free, Made in the like - ness of our God.

cen - te,— A cri - a - ção de Deus.
cen - te,— A cri - a - ção de Deus.

Refrain

F ... G/F ... Em

This clear view of man is per - fect, Seen in all the ra - diance of

Es - sa per - cep - ção do ho - mem, Fei - to à i - ma - gem de

Am Dm ... G7 G7

light; Here we find our na - ture re - vealed, Spir - i - tual and whole

Deus. Nos - sa na - tu - re - za re - ve - la, Es - pi - ri - tu - al

Csus C F ... G/F

in God's sight. This clear view of man is per - fect,

e per - fei - ta. Es - sa per - cep - ção do ho - mem,

Em ... Am Dm

Seen in all the ra - diance of light; Here we find our na - ture re -

Fei - to à i - ma - gem de Deus, Nos - sa na - tu - re - za re -

G7 G7 ... C

vealed, Spir - i - tual and whole in God's sight.

ve - la, Es - pi - ri - tu - al e per - fei - ta.

483

God Guards Me
Elolo nye Mawu elolo ŋutɔ

English
1. God guards me, for my God is Love, Love di - vine.
2. God guides me, for my God is Life, Life di - vine.
3. God rules me, for my God is Truth, Truth di - vine.

Ewe
1. E - lo - lo, nye Ma - wu e - lo - lo ŋu - tɔ,

God loves me: my God is great.
God hides me: from fear and harm.
God knows me, for I am His.

E - ke - ke, mí - do̗ é ɖe dzí.

God guards me, for my God is Love, Love di - vine.
God guides me, for my God is Life, Life di - vine.
God rules me, for my God is Truth, Truth di - vine.

E - lo - lo, nye Ma - wu e - lo - lo ŋu - tɔ,

WORDS: Verse 1 anon. Togo and Ghana; Eng. para. S T Kimbrough Jr., alt.; verses 2, 3 CSPS
MUSIC: Melody from Togo and Ghana; arr. *More Voices*, 2007

11.7.11.7.

Eng. para. vs. 1 © 2004 General Board of Global Ministries, GBG Musik
Eng. vss. 2, 3 © 2017 The Christian Science Board of Directors
Music arr. © 2007 The United Church of Canada (admin. Wood Lake Books)

God loves me: my God is great.
God hides me: from fear and harm.
God knows me, for I am His.
E - ke - ke, mí - dǫ̯é ḑe dzí.

484 God Is Here with Me
Oro aquí con Dios

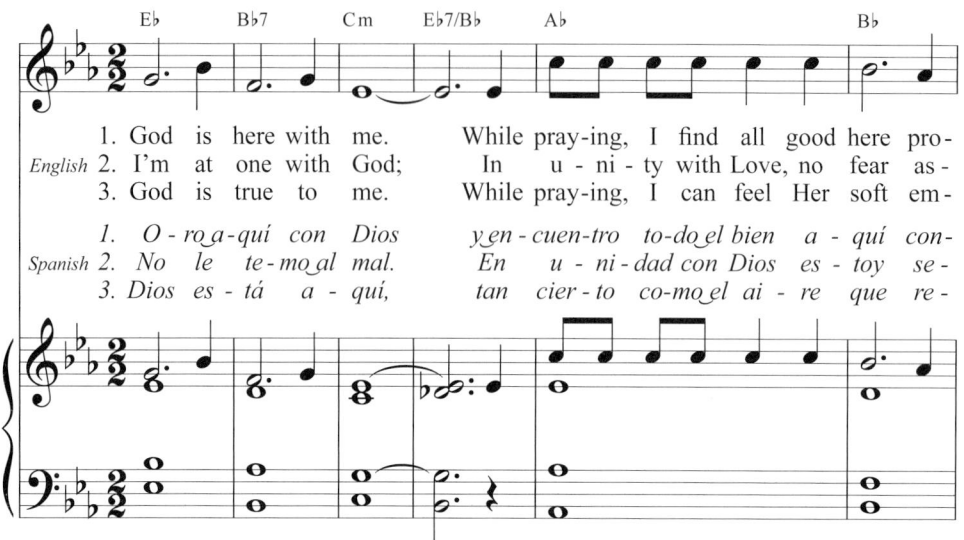

1. God is here with me. While pray-ing, I find all good here pro-
English 2. I'm at one with God; In u - ni - ty with Love, no fear as-
3. God is true to me. While pray-ing, I can feel Her soft em-

1. O - ro_a-quí con Dios y_en - cuen-tro to-do_el bien a - quí con-
Spanish 2. No le te-mo_al mal. En u - ni-dad con Dios es - toy se-
3. Dios es - tá a - quí, tan cier - to co-mo_el ai - re que re-

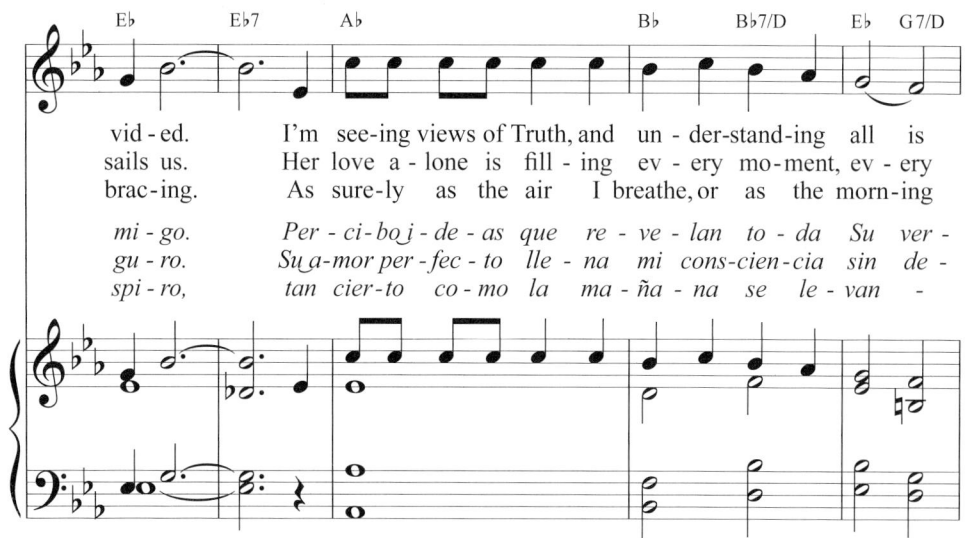

vid - ed. I'm see-ing views of Truth, and un - der-stand-ing all is
sails us. Her love a - lone is fill - ing ev - ery mo-ment, ev - ery
brac-ing. As sure-ly as the air I breathe, or as the morn-ing

mi - go. Per - ci-bo_i - de - as que re - ve-lan to - da Su ver-
gu - ro. Su_a-mor per - fec - to lle - na mi cons-cien-cia sin de-
spi - ro, tan cier-to co - mo la ma - ña - na se le - van -

WORDS: Verses 1, 2 CSPS; verse 3 Javier Gacías; Eng. tr. CSPS
MUSIC: Javier Gacías; harm. Felipe Blycker J.

DIOS ESTÁ AQUÍ
5.11.14.14.

well. In - fir - mi - ty is gone, now leav - ing me per - fect - ly free.
place. My dem-on-stra-tion is com-plete in Her heav - en - ly love.
dawns, Love, ser - e - nad-ing, whis-pers: I will be com-fort-ing you.

dad. Me sien-to li - bre, sin do - len-cia, a-bra-za - do, en paz.
jar Lu - gar al-gu-no en que Su bien no se pue-da ex-pre - sar.
ta, tan cier-to co - mo que Le can-to y me pue-de o - ír.

485 God of Creation and Lord of My Soul

1. God of cre - a - tion and Lord of my soul,
2. You are my wis - dom, and You are my wealth,
3. You and You on - ly are first in my heart;

Be to me ev - er my One and my All. Your
You are my sub - stance, my joy, and my health, My
Ours is a un - ion that nev - er will part. And

pres - ence sur - rounds me by day and by night;
Fa - ther and Moth - er, my ha - ven of peace,
held in Your love, with - out doubt, with - out fear,

This melody comes from an Irish folk song, first published in 1909. The arrangement given here contrasts with the more traditional 4-part setting of the same melody in "Be Thou My Vision" (hymn 442).

WORDS: Fenella Bennetts
MUSIC: Irish melody, Joyce's *Old Irish Folk Music and Songs*, 1909; harm. and arr. CSPS

SLANE
10.10.10.10.
Alternate arr.: 442

While wak - ing or sleep - ing, I live in Your light.
My com - fort, my heal - er, my place of re - lease.
I know now with - in me that heav - en is here.

486 God Sends the Word

1. God sends the Word, the ho-ly Word, And griev-ing hearts are healed; Up-lift-ed they be-hold in light Man's her-i-tage re-vealed;

2. You send Your Word, Your shin-ing Word Of Truth, for-ev-er one, And all man-kind re-joice to know The dream of sor-row done;

3. You send Your Word, Your faith-ful Word, And hosts who toil in vain Re-ject the false-hood a-ges taught And rise to Life a-gain;

Psalms 107:20.

WORDS: Maude DeVerse Newton, adapt., alt.
MUSIC: Suzanne Montgomery

SURETY
8.6.8.6.6.
Alternate tune: 101

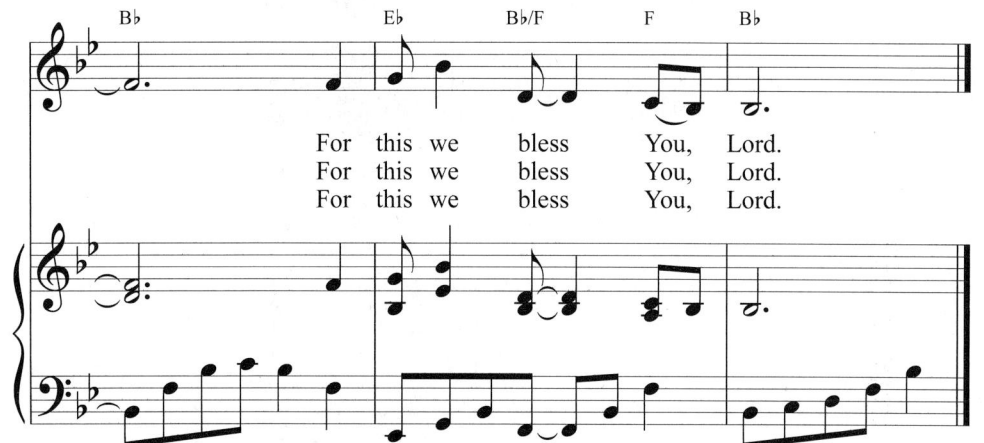

For this we bless You, Lord.
For this we bless You, Lord.
For this we bless You, Lord.

487   Great Is Your Faithfulness

1. Great is Your faith-ful-ness, God, our cre-a-tor,
2. Free-dom from sin and a peace so en-dur-ing,

With You no shad-ow of turn-ing we see.
Your con-stant pres-ence to cheer and to guide.

You do not change, Your com-pas-sions they fail not;
Strength for to-day and bright hope for to-mor-row,

As You have been, You for-ev-er will be.
Such are the bless-ings Your won-ders pro-vide.

Lamentations 3:22, 23 / James 1:17.

WORDS: Thomas O. Chisholm, alt., adapt.
MUSIC: William M. Runyan

FAITHFULNESS
11.10.11.10.Ref.

Refrain

Great is Your faith - ful-ness! Great is Your faith - ful-ness!

Morn - ing by morn - ing new mer - cies I see.

All I have need - ed Your hand has pro - vid - ed.

Great is Your faith - ful - ness, God, un - to me!

488 Guide Me, O Thou Great Jehovah

1. Guide me, O Thou great Je - ho - vah, Pil - grim through this bar - ren land: I am Thine, and Thou art might - y, Hold me with Thy power - ful hand. Bread of heav - en! Bread of heav - en! Feed me now and ev - er - more, Feed me now and ev - er - more.

2. O - pen is the crys - tal foun - tain, Whence the heal - ing wa - ters flow; And the fi - er - y cloud - y pil - lar Leads me all my jour - ney through. Strong De - liv - er - er! Strong De - liv - er - er! Still Thou art my strength and shield, Still Thou art my strength and shield.

Exodus 13:21; 16:4; 17:6 / Nehemiah 9:15, 19 / Psalms 78:14, 16, 24 / John 6:33, 58.

WORDS: William Williams, adapt.; verse 1 tr. Peter Williams; verse 2 tr. William Williams
MUSIC: John Hughes

CWM RHONDDA
8.7.8.7.8.7.7.
Alternate tune: 90

Halle, Halle, Hallelujah

489

Refrain

Hal - le, hal - le, hal - le - lu - jah.

Hal - le, hal - le, hal - le - lu - jah.

Hal - le, hal - le, hal - le - lu - jah, hal - le - lu - jah, hal - le - lu - jah.

end here

Verses

1. Praise God in this ho - ly place, Ev - ery na - tion, ev - ery race.
2. Ev - ery-thing that breathes now praise, Sing your songs, let voic - es raise.

Come, make joy - ful mu - sic to the Lord.
Come, make joy - ful mu - sic to the Lord.

Sound the trum - pet, sound it clear, Sound it for the world to hear.
Play the cym - bals, play the lute; Play the tim - brel, play the flute.

to Refrain

Come, make joy - ful mu - sic to the Lord.
Come, make joy - ful mu - sic to the Lord.

Psalm 150. The refrain of this hymn comes from a traditional Caribbean song, to which composer-arranger Hal Hopson has added new words and music for the verses. The hymn begins with the refrain, which leads directly to verse 1; the refrain is then repeated, followed by verse 2; and the hymn ends with a final statement of the refrain.

WORDS: Para. Psalm 150 Hal H. Hopson
MUSIC: Refrain, Caribbean melody; arr. and additional music Hal H. Hopson
Words and Music © 1998 Hope Publishing Company

HALLE, HALLE
7.7.9.7.7.9.Ref.

490 Hallelujah

WORDS: Para. Psalm 148 Eliot Glaser
MUSIC: Eliot Glaser
Words and Music © 2005 Eliot Glaser

HALLELUYAH
Irregular

praise God, all you hosts. Let them praise God's
praise God, wa - ters high. Let them praise God's

ho - ly name. For God's Word cre - at - ed all.
ho - ly name, Whose glo - ry is o - ver all.

Refrain

Hal - le - lu - jah, hal - le - lu - jah, hal - le - lu - jah, hal - le - lu.

Hal - le - lu - jah, hal - le - lu - jah, hal - le - lu - jah, hal - le - lu. lu.

491 Has Not Your Heart Within You Burned

1. Has not your heart within you burned
   At eve-ning's calm and ho - ly hour,
   As if its in - most depths dis - cerned
   The pres - ence of a loft - ier power?

2. It was the voice of God that spake
   In si - lence to your si - lent heart,
   And bade each high - er thought a - wake,
   And ev - ery dream of earth de - part.

3. O voice of God, for - ev - er near,
   In low, sweet ac - cents whis - pering peace,
   Make us Your har - mo - nies to hear
   Whose heaven - ly ech - oes nev - er cease.

WORDS: Stephen G. Bulfinch, adapt., alt.
MUSIC: Henry Kemble Oliver
Words adapt. © 1932, ren. 1960 The Christian Science Board of Directors

CLONBERNE
L.M.
Alternate tune: 94

He's Got the Whole World

492

1. He's got the whole world in His hands, He's got the
2. He's got the wind and the rain in His hands, He's got the
3. He's got the beasts of the field in His hands, He's got the
4. He's got you and me, broth-er, in His hands, He's got

whole world in His hands, He's got the whole world
wind and the rain in His hands, He's got the wind and the rain
beasts of the field in His hands, He's got the beasts of the field
you and me, sis-ter, in His hands, He's got ev-ery-bod-y here

in His hands, He's got the whole world in His hands.

Psalms 8:7. This hymn can be performed either slowly and reverently, or faster and more upbeat. The rhythmic arrangement given here is designed for a slower performance; for a faster performance, the rhythms in measures 2, 4, and 6 should be changed to begin ♪♩ ♪.

WORDS and MUSIC: African American spiritual; arr. CSPS
Music arr. © 2017 The Christian Science Board of Directors

WHOLE WORLD
Irregular

493   Heaven Is Singing for Joy
El cielo canta alegría

1. Heav-en is sing-ing for joy, Al-le-lu - ia!
English 2. Heav-en is sing-ing for joy, Al-le-lu - ia!
3. Heav-en is sing-ing for joy, Al-le-lu - ia!

1. *El cie-lo can-ta a-le-grí-a, ¡a-le-lu - ya!*
Spanish 2. *El cie-lo can-ta a-le-grí-a, ¡a-le-lu - ya!*
3. *El cie-lo can-ta a-le-grí-a, ¡a-le-lu - ya!*

For your life and mine are bright with the glo - ry of God.
For your life and mine u - nite as ex - pres - sions of Love.
For your life and mine are made for the glo - ry of God.

Por-que en tu vi-da y la mí-a bri - lla la glo - ria de Dios.
Por - que tu vi-da y la mí-a son la ex-pre - sión del A - mor.
Por - que tu vi-da y la mí-a son pa - ra glo - ria de Dios.

Isaiah 55:12. Written in 1958, this is an early example of a hymn that introduces vernacular musical elements, in contrast to the European models predominant in Latin American church music at that time.

WORDS: Pablo Sosa, adapt.; Eng. tr. Pablo Sosa, alt.
MUSIC: Pablo Sosa, alt.

ALEGRÍA
11.13.Alleluias

Refrain

Al – le – lu – ia! Al – le-lu – ia!
¡A – le – lu – ya! ¡A – le-lu – ya!

Al – le – lu – ia! Al – le-lu – ia!
¡A – le – lu – ya! ¡A – le-lu – ya!

494 Holy Bible, Book Divine

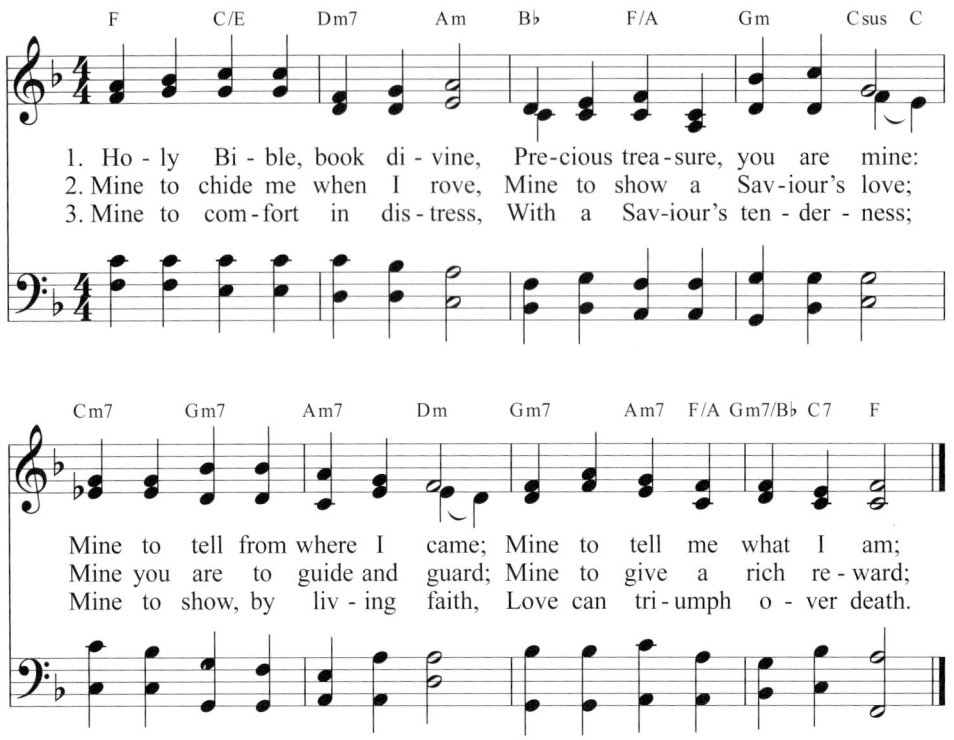

1. Ho-ly Bi-ble, book di-vine, Pre-cious trea-sure, you are mine:
2. Mine to chide me when I rove, Mine to show a Sav-iour's love;
3. Mine to com-fort in dis-tress, With a Sav-iour's ten-der-ness;

Mine to tell from where I came; Mine to tell me what I am;
Mine you are to guide and guard; Mine to give a rich re-ward;
Mine to show, by liv-ing faith, Love can tri-umph o-ver death.

WORDS: John Burton, adapt., alt.
MUSIC: James R. Corbett

HOLY BIBLE
7.7.7.7.
Alternate tune: 114

Holy Spirit, Source of Gladness   495

1. Ho - ly Spir - it, source of glad - ness,
2. Let the Love that knows no mea - sure,
3. Send us Your il - lu - mi - na - tion;

Come with all Your ra - diance bright;
Now in quick - ening showers de - scend;
Ban - ish all our fears at length;

Lift all bur - dens and all sad - ness;
Bring to us the rich - est trea - sure
Rest up - on this con - gre - ga - tion,

O'er Your chil - dren shed Your light.
We could wish or God can send.
Spir - it of un - fail - ing strength.

The unique rhythmic feel of this hymn results from alternating 6/4 and 3/2 meters. With the quarter-note constant, both meters are the same length; but the 6/4 measures divide those quarter-notes into 2 groups of 3, whereas the 3/2 measures divide into 3 groups of 2.

WORDS: Paul Gerhardt; tr. John Christian Jacobi, adapt.
MUSIC: Paul Sophus Rung-Keller
Music © 1949 Paul Sophus Rung-Keller

KIRKEN ER SOM HIMMERIGE
8.7.8.7.
Alternate tune: 119

496 Holy Spirit, Light Divine

1. Ho-ly Spir-it, Light di-vine, Shine up-on this heart of mine; Kin-dle ev-ery high de-sire; Cleanse my thought in Your pure fire. Ho-ly Spir-it,

2. Ho-ly Spir-it, Peace di-vine, Still this rest-less heart of mine; Speak to calm the toss-ing sea, Stayed in Your tran-quil-i-ty. Ho-ly Spir-it,

3. Ho-ly Spir-it, all di-vine, Dwell with-in this heart of mine; Bid my trou-bled thoughts be still; With Your peace my spir-it fill. Ho-ly Spir-it,

This hymn works well when performed with a straightforward rhythmic approach; however, a gentle swing rhythm is appropriate and in keeping with the composers' original intention.

WORDS: Andrew Reed and Samuel Longfellow, adapt., alt.
MUSIC: Laura Lapointe and Stephen Lapointe, alt.

SPIRIT
7.7.7.7.D.
Alternate tune: 118

497 Home Is the Consciousness of Good

1. Home is the con - scious - ness of good That holds us
2. Our Fa - ther's house has man - y rooms, And each with
3. Home is the Fa - ther's sweet "Well done," God's dai - ly,

in its wide em - brace; The stead - y light that com - forts
peace and love im - bued; No child can ev - er stray be -
hour - ly gift of grace. We go to meet our neigh - bor's

us In ev - ery path our foot - steps trace.
yond The com - pass of in - fin - i - tude.
need, And find our home in ev - ery place.

Matthew 25:21 / John 14:2. This music is called "O Waly Waly," because it is traditionally linked to words from a Scottish folk song. Those words originated with a different melody; the origin of this melody, though certainly British, remains obscure. In the 20th century it received widespread musical treatment from musicians as diverse as Benjamin Britten and Pete Seeger. The words to this hymn are from a poem entitled "Home," originally printed in the October 15, 1938 issue of the *Christian Science Sentinel*.

WORDS: Rosemary C. Cobham, alt.
MUSIC: British melody; harm. and arr. Robert Rockabrand
Music arr. © 2008 The Christian Science Board of Directors

O WALY WALY
L.M.
Alternate arr: 588

How Firm a Foundation 498

1. How firm a foun - da - tion, you saints of the Lord,
2. Fear not, I am with you, O be not dis - mayed,
3. When through fier - y tri - als your path - way shall lie,

Is laid for your faith in His ex - cel - lent Word.
For I am your God, I will still give you aid;
My grace, all suf - fi - cient, shall be your sup - ply;

What more can He say than to you He has said,
I'll strength - en you, help you, and cause you to stand,
The flame shall not hurt you; I on - ly de - sign

To you who to God for your ref - uge have fled:
Up - held by My gra - cious, om - ni - po - tent hand;
Your dross to con - sume and your gold to re - fine.

Isaiah 41:10; 43:2 / II Corinthians 12:9. Although this text is most commonly joined with ADESTE FIDELES (hymn 123), it is commonly combined with the shape-note melody given here, a coupling that originates in hymnals from the mid-19th century.

WORDS: Rippon's *A Selection of Hymns*, 1787, adapt., alt.
MUSIC: American melody, Funk's *Genuine Church Music*, 1832; harm. CSPS

FOUNDATION
11.11.11.11.
Alternate tune: 123

499   I Am the Lord

1. I am the Lord, there is none else; There is no God be-
2. I am the Truth, there is none else; There is no Truth be-
3. In-no-cent one, sin-less and pure, Noth-ing can ev-er di-

side Me. I gird-ed thee, I gird-ed thee,
side Me. In-fi-nite light, boun-ti-ful, bright,
vide thee. Gov-erned by Love, you are se-cure;

Though thou hast not e-ven known Me. But know that from the
Is ev-er pres-ent to guide thee. Be-loved and free, e-
I am for-ev-er be-side thee. So rest and know wher-

Isaiah 45:5, 6.

WORDS and MUSIC: Désirée Goyette, words alt.
Words and Music © 2008 Lightchild Publishing

I AM THE LORD
Irregular

ris - ing sun To the west there is none be - side Me, For
ter - nal - ly, Per - fect peace and joy I pro - vide thee, For
e'er you go, Home and heaven can - not be de - nied thee, For

I am the Lord, there is none else; There is no God be - side Me.

500   I Awake Each Morn

1. I a-wake each morn to a brand-new day, Sing-ing
2. (I can) walk with Love through the val-ley of fear, Sing-ing

Hal - le - lu - jah! as I go on my way, For my
Hal - le - lu - jah! O, my Sav - ior is here! For my

heart is fixed on this one guar - an - tee: The
emp - ty long - ing no hope can ful - fill, But

Love that is All holds me ten - der - ly.
Love meets all need and bids want be still.

Refrain

Ten - der mer - cies, oh ten - der mer - cies, Ten - der

mer - cies are hold - ing me. Ten - der mer - cies, oh

ten - der mer - cies, Ten - der mer - cies are hold - ing me. 2. I can

Psalms 23:4.

WORDS and MUSIC: Susan Booth Mack Snipes
Words and Music © 2007 In Our Field Productions

DALTON
Irregular

501 I Love Your Way of Freedom, Lord

1. I love Your way of free-dom, Lord, To serve You is my choice;
2. Though storm or dis-cord cross my path Your power is still my stay,

In Your clear light of Truth I rise And, lis-tening for Your voice,
Though hu - man will and woe would check My up - ward-soar-ing way;

I hear Your prom-ise old and new, That bids all fear to cease:
All un - a - fraid I wait, the while Your an - gels bring re - lease,

"My pres-ence still shall go with you And I will give you peace."
For still Your pres-ence is with me, And You do give me peace.

3. I climb, with joy, the heights of Mind, To soar o'er time and space;

I yet shall know as I am known And see You face to face.

Till time and space and fear are naught My quest shall nev - er cease,

Your pres-ence ev - er goes with me And You do give me peace.

Exodus 33:14 / I Corinthians 13:12.

WORDS: Violet Hay, alt.
MUSIC: Andrew D. Brewis
FOCUS
C.M.D.
Alternate tune: 136

I Place Them in Your Hands 502

1. I place them in Your hands, dear God,
2. You cher - ish and You guard them all
3. Your love, far great - er than my own,

I trust them to Your care,
From snares of ev - ery kind.
Pro - vides for them all good.

The One who marks the spar - row's fall
No false re - spon - si - bil - i - ty
This have I learned— to hum - bly trust

And num - bers ev - ery hair.
Dis - turbs my peace of mind.
Your fa - ther - moth - er - hood.

Psalms 84:3 / Luke 21:18. These words are from a poem entitled "Prayer for Loved Ones," first published in the May 1983 issue of *The Christian Science Journal*.

WORDS: Helen C. Benson, alt.
MUSIC: S. Allen
ABBY
C.M.
Words © 1983 The Christian Science Board of Directors

503   I Walk with Love

1. I walk with Love a-long the way, And
2. Let's walk with Love a-long the way, And
3. Come, walk with Love a-long the way, Let

O, it is a ho-ly day; No
talk with Love and Love o-bey. God's
child-like trust be yours to-day; Up-

more I suf-fer cru-el fear, I
heal-ing truth is free to all, And
lift your thought, with cour-age go, Give

WORDS: Minny M. H. Ayers, alt.
MUSIC: Mindy Jostyn, alt.

WELLESLEY
8.8.8.8.8.8.
Alternate tunes: 139, 427

504 I Want to Know the Truth

Eu quero a Verdade conhecer

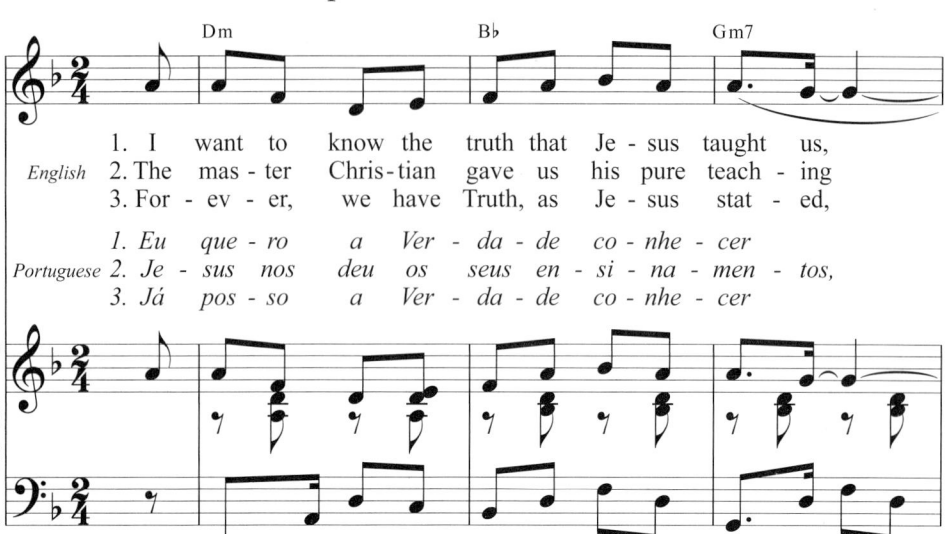

English
1. I want to know the truth that Je-sus taught us,
2. The mas-ter Chris-tian gave us his pure teach-ing
3. For-ev-er, we have Truth, as Je-sus stat-ed,

Portuguese
1. Eu que-ro a Ver-da-de co-nhe-cer
2. Je-sus nos deu os seus en-si-na-men-tos,
3. Já pos-so a Ver-da-de co-nhe-cer

To taste the lib-er-ty his prom-ise
And guid-ed us in heal-ing and in
The Soul that gives the joy we've all a-

Al-me-jo a li-ber-da-de re-ce-
Cu-ran-do os do-en-tes e a-
E a Al-ma re-fle-tir com a-le-

WORDS: Leide Lessa; Eng. tr. CSPS
MUSIC: Jaci Maraschin

LAVAPES
11.11.11.11.

505 I Will Bless the Lord

Psalms 145:1, 8, 17. The hymn is to be sung all the way through, followed by a return to the refrain. The fermata at the end of the refrain, indicating the proper endpoint, applies only to the second time through.

WORDS and MUSIC: Frank Hernandez

Words and Music © 1981 Frank Hernandez (admin. Bridgestone Multimedia Group, LLC)

I WILL BLESS THE LORD
9.8.9.7.Ref.

506 I Will Come Before the Lord

1. I will come be-fore the Lord In the still - ness of the morn-ing; When gold - en dawn shines on the earth And I feel Love's ten - der pres-ence. You are my morn-ing song.

2. I will come be-fore the Lord In the bright - ness of the mid - day; In rush - ing life and flood of sound I can find Soul's qui - et ha - ven. You are my mid-day song.

3. I will come be-fore the Lord In the soft - ness of the eve - ning When na - ture bathes in pur - ple light; I give thanks for Spir - it's bless-ings. You are my eve-ning song.

4. I will come be-fore the Lord In the dark - ness of the mid - night When moon and stars are shin-ing clear; I feel good - ness pres - ent with me. You are my mid-night song.

5. Day and night, You are my song And we sweet - ly sing to- geth-er To wor - ship, love, and praise Your name, Sing-ing in Your house for - ev - er. Day and night, You are my song.

WORDS: Charlene A. Beck, alt.
MUSIC: Scottish melody; arr. CSPS

WILD MOUNTAIN THYME
Irregular

I'm Gonna Live So God Can Use Me 507

1. I'm gon-na live so God can use me (I'm gon-na live so) (God can use me) an-y time, (an-y time,) and an-y-where. (an-y-where.)

I'm gon-na live so God can use me (I'm gon-na live so) (God can use me) an-y time, (an-y time,) and an-y-where. (an-y-where.)

2. I'm gonna work so
God can use me
any time, and anywhere.
(2 times)

3. I'm gonna pray so
God can use me
any time, and anywhere.
(2 times)

4. I'm gonna sing so
God can use me
any time, and anywhere.
(2 times)

A special feature of this music is the presence of echoes throughout. These textual repetitions do not affect the melody, but those singing other parts may choose to sing the words in parentheses.

WORDS and MUSIC: African American spiritual; harm. and arr. CSPS

Music arr. © 2017 The Christian Science Board of Directors

I'M GONNA LIVE
9.7.9.7.

508   I've Got Peace Like a River

1. I've got peace like a riv-er, I've got peace like a riv-er,
2. I've got joy like a foun-tain, I've got joy like a foun-tain,
3. I've got love like an o-cean, I've got love like an o-cean,
4. I've got faith like an an-chor, I've got faith like an an-chor,

I've got peace like a riv-er in my soul.
I've got joy like a foun-tain in my soul.
I've got love like an o-cean in my soul.
I've got faith like an an-chor in my soul.

I've got peace like a riv-er, I've got peace like a riv-er,
I've got joy like a foun-tain, I've got joy like a foun-tain,
I've got love like an o-cean, I've got love like an o-cean,
I've got faith like an an-chor, I've got faith like an an-chor,

I've got peace like a riv-er in my soul.
I've got joy like a foun-tain in my soul.
I've got love like an o-cean in my soul.
I've got faith like an an-chor in my soul.

Isaiah 66:12 / Galatians 5:22, 23 / Hebrews 6:19.

WORDS and MUSIC: African American spiritual; harm. CSPS
Music harm. © 2017 The Christian Science Board of Directors

PEACE LIKE A RIVER
7.7.10.D.

In Christ There Is No East or West 509

1. In Christ there is no East or West, In
2. In Christ shall pure hearts ev - ery - where Their
3. In Christ now meet both East and West, In

Christ no South or North; But one great fam - i -
true com - mu - nion find; God's ser - vice is the
Christ meet South and North; One joy - ous, true com -

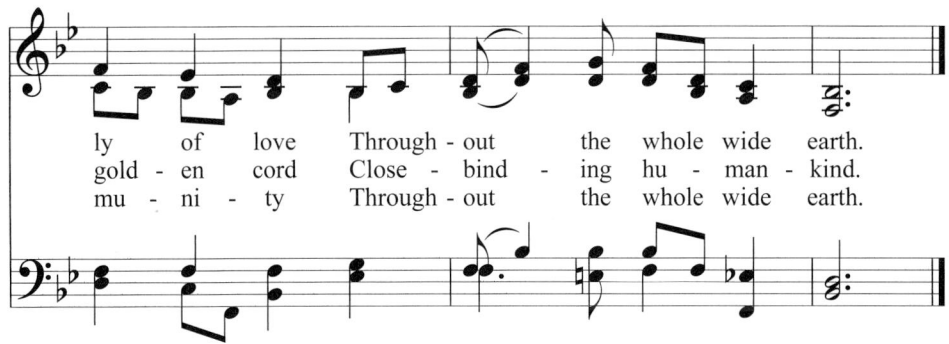

ly of love Through - out the whole wide earth.
gold - en cord Close - bind - ing hu - man - kind.
mu - ni - ty Through - out the whole wide earth.

Galatians 3:28. Given here in the popular arrangement created by Henry T. Burleigh in 1939, this tune—adopted, and no doubt adapted, in the 19th century by African American slaves—is purportedly of Irish origin. Burleigh's connection with this music traces to his grandmother, a former slave, from whom he learned several traditional songs.

WORDS: John Oxenham, adapt. Grace Moore, Nancy Krody, and Ruth Duck
MUSIC: African-American spiritual, Marsh's *Jubilee Songs*, 1876; adapt. and harm. Harry T. Burleigh
McKEE
C.M.

510   In Love Divine

1. In Love di - vine all earth-born fear and sor - row Fade as the
2. And as on wings of faith we soar and wor-ship, Held by God's
3. Then in this ra - diant light of ad - o - ra - tion, We know that

dark when dawn pours forth her light; And un - der-
love a - bove the shad-ows dim, Hushed in the
man be - loved is in God's care, Not wrapped in

stand - ing prayer is ful - ly an - swered, When trust-ing-
gran - deur of a heart's a - wak - ening, Un - folds a
fear nor bowed with tir - ed la - bor, But sat - is -

WORDS: Susan F. Campbell
MUSIC: Benjamin Russell Vaughan

WINGS
11.10.11.10.
Alternate tunes: 149, 426

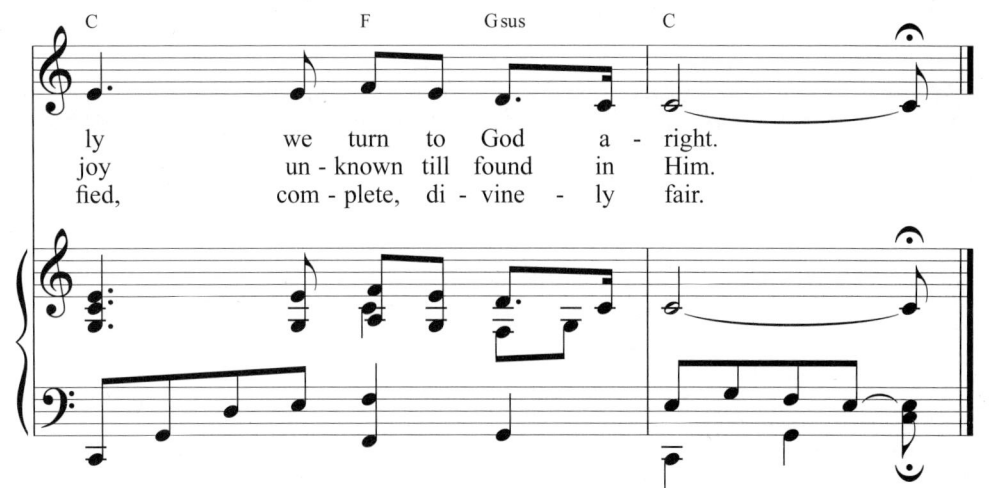

ly   we turn to God a - right.
joy   un - known till found in Him.
fied,   com - plete, di - vine - ly fair.

511 It Came upon the Midnight Clear

1. It came up-on the mid-night clear, That glo-rious song of old,
2. O ye be-neath life's crush-ing load Whose forms are bend-ing low,
3. For lo, the days are has-tening on, By proph-ets seen of old,

The an-gels, bend-ing near the earth, Their won-drous sto-ry told
Who toil a-long the climb-ing way With pain-ful steps and slow;
When with the ev-er-cir-cling years Shall come the time fore-told;

Of peace on earth, good will to men, From heaven's all-gra-cious King;
Look now, for glad and gold-en hours Come swift-ly on the wing;
When the new heaven and earth shall own The Prince of Peace their King,

The world in sol-emn still-ness lay To hear the an-gels sing.
O rest be-side the wea-ry road, And hear the an-gels sing.
And all the world send back the song Which now the an-gels sing.

Isaiah 9:6 / Luke 2:13, 14 / Revelation 21:1. This setting of the familiar carol has become popular in the United States and elsewhere.

WORDS: Edmund H. Sears, adapt.
MUSIC: Richard Storrs Willis

CAROL
C.M.D.
Alternate tunes: 158, 159, 512

It Came upon the Midnight Clear   512

1. It came up-on the mid-night clear, That glo-rious song of old,
2. O ye be-neath life's crush-ing load Whose forms are bend-ing low,
3. For lo, the days are has-tening on, By proph-ets seen of old,

The an-gels, bend-ing near the earth, Their won-drous sto-ry told
Who toil a-long the climb-ing way With pain-ful steps and slow;
When with the ev-er-cir-cling years Shall come the time fore-told;

Of peace on earth, good will to men, From heaven's all-gra-cious King;
Look now, for glad and gold-en hours Come swift-ly on the wing;
When the new heaven and earth shall own The Prince of Peace their King,

The world in sol-emn still-ness lay To hear the an-gels sing.
O rest be-side the wea-ry road, And hear the an-gels sing.
And all the world send back the song Which now the an-gels sing.

Isaiah 9:6 / Luke 2:13, 14 / Revelation 21:1. This setting of the familiar carol is well established in the United Kingdom, and throughout the British Commonwealth.

WORDS: Edmund H. Sears, adapt.
MUSIC: English melody, Sullivan's *Church Hymns with Tunes*, 1874; harm. Arthur S. Sullivan

NOEL
C.M.D.
Alternate tunes: 158, 159, 511

513 It Matters Not What Be Thy Lot

"Satisfied" by Mary Baker Eddy

1. It mat-ters not   what be thy lot,   So Love doth
3. Aye, dark-ling sense,   a-rise, go hence! Our God is

guide;   For storm or shine,   pure peace is thine, What-
good.   False fears are foes—   truth tat-ters those, When

e'er   be - tide.   2. And of these stones, or
un - der - stood.   4. Love loos-eth thee, and

ty-rants' thrones, God a - ble is   To raise up seed— in
lift-eth me,   A - yont hate's thrall: There Life is light, and

thought and   deed—   To faith - ful   His.
wis - dom   might,   And God is   All.

5. The cen-turies break, the earth-bound wake,   God's glo - ri - fied!

Who doth His will—   His like-ness still—   Is sat - is - fied.

Who doth His will—   His like-ness still—   Is sat - is - fied.

WORDS: Mary Baker Eddy
MUSIC: Andrew D. Brewis
Music © 2008 The Christian Science Board of Directors

MKHAYA
8.4.8.4.
Alternate tunes: 160–162, 514, 515

It Matters Not What Be Thy Lot 514

"Satisfied" by Mary Baker Eddy

1. It mat-ters not what be thy lot, So Love doth guide; For storm or shine, pure peace is thine, What-e'er be-tide. 2. And of these stones, or ty-rants' thrones, God a-ble is To raise up seed— in thought and deed— To faith-ful His. 3. Aye, dark-ling sense, a-rise, go hence! Our God is good. False fears are foes— truth tat-ters those, When un-der-stood. 4. Love

(4.) loos-eth thee, and lift-eth me, A-yont hate's thrall: There Life is light, and wis-dom might, And God is All. 5. The cen-turies break, the earth-bound wake, God's glo-ri-fied! Who doth His will— His like-ness still— Is sat-is-fied.

WORDS: Mary Baker Eddy
MUSIC: Mindy Jostyn; arr. CSPS
Music © 1998 The Christian Science Board of Directors
Music arr. © 2017 The Christian Science Board of Directors

HUDSON
8.4.8.4.
Alternate tunes 160–162, 513, 515

515   It Matters Not What Be Thy Lot

"Satisfied" by Mary Baker Eddy

1. It mat-ters not what be thy lot, So Love doth guide; For
4. Love loos-eth thee, and lift-eth me, A-yont hate's thrall: There

storm or shine, pure peace is thine, What-e'er be-tide. 2. And
Life is light, and wis-dom might, And God is All. 5. The

of these stones, or ty-rants' thrones, God a-ble is To
cen-turies break, the earth-bound wake, God's glo-ri-fied! Who

WORDS: Mary Baker Eddy
MUSIC: Ryan Vigil
Music © 2017 The Christian Science Board of Directors

GRATITUDE
8.4.8.4.
Alternate tunes 160–162, 513, 514

end here

raise up seed— in thought and deed—To faith - ful His.
doth His will— His like - ness still— Is sat - is - fied.

3. Aye, dark - ling sense, a - rise, go hence! Our God is good. False

to beginning

fears are foes— truth tat - ters those, When un - der - stood.

516 It's True: God Is Good

C'est vrai: Dieu est bon

This refrain is based on a traditional Congolese song; new verses (with new but related music) have been added.

WORDS: Refrain anon. Congo; Eng. tr. CSPS; Fr. tr. David Fines; Fr. verses CSPS, incl. Eng. tr.
MUSIC: Refrain Congolese melody; arr. and verse music Jeremy Carper

5.5.5.6.Ref.

Fr. tr. ref. © 2005 David Fines
Fr. Words vss. 1–3, Eng. tr., Music arr. ref., vs. music © 2017 The Christian Science Board of Directors

Verses

1. Know that God is here, Know that
2. God and man at one, Man is
3. Feel God's mer - cy true, Feel the

1. Dieu est tou - jours pré - sent. Nous som - mes
2. Dieu et hom - me u - nis, L'hom - me, Son
3. Oh Dieu, Ta com - pas - sion, Ton Es - prit,

we are dear, We are in His care,
God's own son, Love's work now is done,
Spir - it new. Love Her will to do,

Ses en - fants Qu'Il ai - me ten - dre - ment,
fils ché - ri. Son œu - vre est ac - com - plie.
nous sen - tons. Nous Te re - flé - tons.

to Refrain

God is good, God is good.

Dieu est bon, Dieu est bon.

517 Joyfully We're Singing
Canto de alegría

English
1. Joy - ful - ly we're sing - ing of our dear God's grace,
2. Who can sep - a - rate us from the love of God?
3. Ev - 'ry - thing that hap - pens to us day by day,
4. God re - mains our ref - uge in the trials we face,

Spanish
1. *Can - to de a - le - grí - a por - que ten - go a - mor.*
2. *Del a - mor de Dios, ¿quién me se - pa - ra - rá?*
3. *To - do lo que es bue - no pa - sa en mi vi - da a - quí*
4. *En to - das las prue - bas Dios me a - yu - da - rá.*

Liv - ing ev - 'ry day with - in Love's warm em - brace.
Truth is here to shield us with its staff and rod.
Christ will be the bea - con that will light our way.
Shield - ing and sus - tain - ing us with lov - ing grace.

Vi - vo ca - da dí - a con el Se - ñor.
Es - con - di - do en Dios, ¿quién me to - ca - rá?
Dios me lo pre - pa - ra y me pro - te - ge a - sí.
No me de - sam - pa - ra, no me de - ja - rá.

Ea - ger - ly we long to wit - ness ev - 'ry - where;
What is there to harm us when this help is sure?
Through dis - tress and per - il, God is faith - ful still,
Work - ing through the la - bors of our hearts and hands,

Quie - ro a to - do el mun - do de Él siem - pre ha - blar.
Si Dios jus - ti - fi - ca, ¿quién con - de - na - rá?
En las prue - bas du - ras, Dios me es siem - pre fiel:
Él me ne - ce - si - ta en Su o - bra ya.

All through - out the world, God's sav - ing love to share.
We are more than con - quer - ors; we rest se - cure.
Why should we be fear - ful if we trust God's will?
Truth will lead us on - ward in tri - um - phant bands!

Quie - ro a to - do el mun - do Su a - mor do - nar.
Si Dios me de - fien - de, ¿quién me a - cu - sa - rá?
¿por qué te - ner du - das, si des - can - so en Él?
Se - gui - ré a - de - lan - te, voy a tri - un - far.

Romans 8:35, 37–39.

WORDS: Verses 1, 4 anon.; verses 2, 3 Enrique S. Turrall; Eng. tr. Mary Louise Bringle, adapt.
MUSIC: Argentine melody; harm. Ronald Krisman, alt.

ARGENTINA
11.11.11.11.Ref.

Eng. tr. and Music harm. © 2005 GIA Publications, Inc.

Refrain

Sing - ing of our dear God's grace,
Can - to por - que ten - go_a - mor.

Liv - ing in Love's warm em - brace,
Vi - vo con el Se - ñor.

Long - ing, now and ev - 'ry - where,
Quie - ro de Él siem - pre_ha - blar.

All God's sav - ing love to share.
Quie - ro Su a - mor do - nar.

518 Know, O Child, Your Full Salvation

1. Know, O child, your full salva - tion; Rise o'er
sin and fear and care; Joy to find, in ev - ery
sta - tion, Some - thing still to do, or bear.

2. Think what spir - it dwells with - in you; Think what
Fa - ther's smiles are yours; Think what Je - sus did to
show you: Spir - it's prom - ise lifts, re - stores.

3. Has - ten on from grace to glo - ry, Armed with
faith and winged with prayer; Heaven's e - ter - nal day be -
fore you, God's own hand shall guide you there.

4. So ful - fill your ho - ly mis - sion, Safe - ly
pass through pil - grim - days, Hope shall grow to full fru -
i - tion, Faith to sight and prayer to praise.

WORDS: Henry Francis Lyte, adapt., alt.
MUSIC: Nicholas P. Schliapin

MISSION
8.7.8.7.
Alternate tunes: 166, 167

Lean on the Sustaining Infinite   519

1. Lean on the sus-tain-ing in - fi - nite And bless-ings will be yours.
2. Let the heal-ing reign of Truth and Life, The reign of Love di - vine,
3. Love with a heart of ten - der-ness Your en - e - mies and friends;

Lean not on per - son, place, or thing, Or e - co - nom - ic laws;
Be now es - tab-lished with - in me To show Soul's clear de - sign
How - ev - er hard this may ap-pear, This qual - i - ty just mends.

But lean up - on all - bless-ing God Who will all needs sup-ply
Of One-ness, in - di - vis - i - ble— Of God and me as one—
For Love is God in ac - tion true, A pres-ence that is felt;

And give to all a - bun-dant good That mon - ey can-not buy.
As wa - ter is to o - cean wave, As sun-beam is to sun.
A heal-ing and a sav-ing power That will all dis-cord melt.

4. So lean, and let, and love; This is the bal - anced Way.

It's free from self - will, pres-sure, stress; It wel-comes in God's day.

The lean - ing is so gen-tle; The let-ting is so free.

And lov - ing is the on - ly way To think, and speak, and be.

The words of this hymn are from a poem entitled "Three I's for life," printed in the January 13, 2013 issue of the *Christian Science Sentinel*. The poem references the opening line of *Science and Health with Key to The Scriptures*, by Mary Baker Eddy: "To those leaning on the sustaining infinite, to-day is big with blessings."

WORDS: Jill Gooding, alt.
MUSIC: Andrew D. Brewis

SUSTAINING
Irregular

Words © 2013 The Christian Science Board of Directors
Words alt. and Music © 2017 The Christian Science Board of Directors

520 Let All Things Now Living

1. Let all things now liv-ing A song of thanks-giv-ing
2. By law God en - for-ces, The stars in their cours-es

To God our cre - a - tor tri - um-phant-ly raise;
And sun in its or - bit o - be-dient-ly shine;

Who fash-ioned and made us, Pro - tect-ed and stayed us,
The hills and the moun-tains, The riv - ers and foun-tains,

By guid - ing us for - ward through-out all our days.
The depths of the o - cean pro - claim God di - vine.

Exodus 13:21 / Judges 5:20 / Nehemiah 9:19 / Psalm 148. This melody is derived from an old tune first published in Edward Jones's *The Bardic Museum* (1802), a compilation of "musical, poetical, and historical relicks of the Welsh Bards and Druids." In that volume the tune is entitled "Llwyn-onn," "the name of Mr. Jones's mansion, near Wrexham in Denbighshire."

WORDS: Katherine K. Davis, alt., adapt.
MUSIC: Welsh melody, Jones's *The Bardic Museum*, 1802; harm. CSPS

ASH GROVE
6.6.11.6.6.11.D.

521   Let There Be Peace on Earth

WORDS: Jill Jackson, alt.
MUSIC: Sy Miller; harm. Charles H. Webb
Words and Music © 1955, ren. 1983 Jan-Lee Music

WORLD PEACE
Irregular

522   Lift Up the Door

Macht hoch die Tür

English
1. Lift up the door, the might-y gates, Be-hold, the King of Glo-ry waits! Our King of kings is draw-ing near; The Mak-er of the world is here. Life and sal-va-tion
2. A God of help, in-teg-ri-ty, Whose char-i-ot's hu-mil-i-ty, His king-ly crown is ho-li-ness, His scep-ter, mer-cy, all to bless— To ev'-ry woe an
3. Oh, bless the na-tion, bless the town, That holds this King in high re-nown. Oh, bless a-like the heart and mind Whose love for God to-geth-er bind. His right-eous-ness will

German
1. Macht hoch die Tür, die Tor' macht weit, es kommt der Herr der Herr-lich-keit, ein Kö-nig al-ler Kö-nig-reich', ein Hei-land al-ler Welt zu-gleich, der Heil und Le-ben
2. Er ist ge-recht, ein Hel-fer wert, Sanft-mü-tig-keit ist Sein Ge-fährt, Sein Kö-nigs-kron' ist Hei-lig-keit, Sein Zep-ter ist Barm-her-zig-keit. All uns-re Not zum
3. O wohl dem Land, o wohl der Stadt, so die-sen Kö-nig bei sich hat! Wohl al-len Her-zen ins-ge-mein, da die-ser Kö-nig zie-het ein! Er ist die rech-te

This advent hymn, which has been popular in Germany since at least the early 18th century, was translated into English in 1855 and has since appeared in many British and American hymnals.

WORDS: Para. Psalm 24 Georg Weissel; verses 1, 2 Eng. tr. Catherine Winkworth, adapt.;   MACHT HOCH DIE TÜR
verse 3 Eng. tr. CSPS   8.8.8.8.8.8.8.6.6.
MUSIC: German melody, Freylinghausen's *Geistreiches Gesangbuch*, 1704; harm. Annette Ruth Söllinger
Eng. tr. adapt. vss. 1–2, Eng. tr. vs. 3, Music harm. © 2017 The Christian Science Board of Directors

523 Like as a Mother, God Comforts All Her Children

1. Like as a moth-er, God com-forts all Her chil - dren;
2. Love is true so - lace in giv - ing joy for sor - row,—
3. O ho - ly pres - ence, that stills all our de-mand - ing,

Com - fort is calm, that bids all tu-mult cease;
O, in that light, all earth - ly loss is gain;
O love of God, that needs but to be known!

Com - fort is hope and cour - age for en -
Joy must en - dure, Love's giv - ing is for -
Heaven is at hand, when Your pure touch per -

Isaiah 66:13.

WORDS: Maria Louise Baum, alt.
MUSIC: Suzanne Montgomery

SOLACE
12.10.11.10.
Alternate tune: 174

deav - or,
ev - er;
suades us,

Com-fort is love, whose home a - bides in
Life is of God, whose ra-diance can-not
Com-fort of God, that seeks and finds Her

peace.
wane.

own.

524 Like a River That Runs to the Ocean

WORDS: Mindy Jostyn, alt.
MUSIC: Mindy Jostyn; arr. CSPS

ONE
Irregular

Lord, I Want to Be a Christian 525

1. Lord, I want to be a Chris-tian In my heart, in my heart;
2. Lord, I want to be more lov-ing In my heart, in my heart;
3. Lord, I want to be more ho-ly In my heart, in my heart;
4. Lord, I want to be like Je-sus In my heart, in my heart;

Lord, I want to be a Chris-tian In my heart.
Lord, I want to be more lov-ing In my heart.
Lord, I want to be more ho-ly In my heart.
Lord, I want to be like Je-sus In my heart.

In my heart, in my heart,
(in my heart,) (in my heart,)

Lord, I want to be a Chris-tian In my heart.
Lord, I want to be more lov-ing In my heart.
Lord, I want to be more ho-ly In my heart.
Lord, I want to be like Je-sus In my heart.

The third line of this African American spiritual makes effective use of echoes; while the melody holds out the word "heart," those singing lower parts may like to repeat the words "in my heart" to the new music.

WORDS and MUSIC: African American spiritual; harm. CSPS
Music harm. © 2017 The Christian Science Board of Directors

I WANT TO BE A CHRISTIAN
8.6.8.3.6.8.3.

526 Lo! As We Follow After Good

Unison

1. Lo! as we fol-low af-ter good, We find God's word is un-der-stood,
2. O you to whom God's word is shown, Make all His prom-is-es your own,

Harmony ... *Unison*

So we prove Him, Praise and prove Him! Through us He does per-form His will, To us His prom-is-es ful-fil,
Rise and prove Him, Praise and prove Him! His might-y love and ho-ly power Are here to bless us ev-ery hour,

Harmony

For we love Him! Praise and love Him! Al-le-
Let us love Him! Praise and love Him! Al-le-

This arrangement of the 17th-century German melody "Lasst uns erfreuen" is credited to Ralph Vaughan Williams, editor of *The English Hymnal* (1906), in which it first appeared. Best known for his songs and symphonic works, Vaughan Williams, alongside Edward Elgar, is considered to be one of the most important English composers of the early 20th century.

WORDS: Violet Hay, alt.
MUSIC: German melody, *Geistliche Kirchengesäng*, 1623; harm and arr. Ralph Vaughan Williams
LASST UNS ERFREUEN
8.8.4.4.D.Alleluias

lu   –   ia,   Al - le - lu   –   ia,   Al - le - lu   –   ia!
lu   –   ia,   Al - le - lu   –   ia,   Al - le - lu   –   ia!

527   Lord, ... Open His Eyes

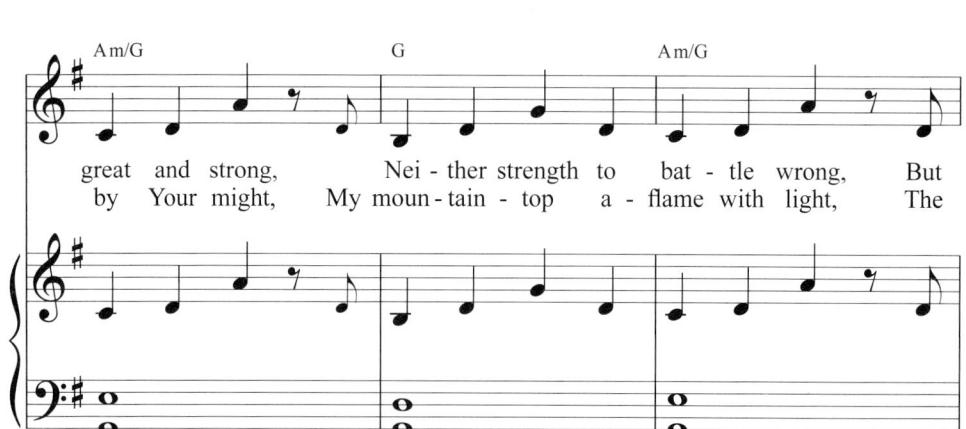

1. "Lord, ... o-pen his eyes, that he may see," The might-y proph-et prayed. Send not ar-mies great and strong, Nei-ther strength to bat-tle wrong, But
2. Lord, o-pen my eyes that I may see Your pres-ence ev-ery - where, My dwell-ing cir-cled by Your might, My moun-tain-top a-flame with light, The

II Kings 6:17. The words of this hymn are from a poem entitled "Vision," printed in the December 17, 1960 issue of the *Christian Science Sentinel*.

WORDS: Elizabeth Glass Barlow, alt.
MUSIC: Désirée Goyette

REGAL GLEN
Irregular

Words © 1960, ren. 1988 The Christian Science Board of Directors
Music © 2016 The Christian Science Board of Directors

528 Lord, Your Mercy Reaches Higher

1. Lord, Your mer-cy reach-es high-er than the heav-ens;
2. Lord, Your right-eous-ness is stead-fast as the moun-tains;
3. Lord, Your chil-dren shall be sat-is-fied with glad-ness;

Lord, Your faith-ful-ness is wid-er than the sky.
Lord, Your good-ness is a riv-er with-out end.
Joy and peace a-bun-dant is their her-i-tage.

Lord, Your gra-cious judg-ments, deep-er than the earth,
Lord, Your lov-ing-kind-ness is a won-drous thing;
Life flows from Your pres-ence, ra-di-ant and new;

Show Your ten-der care for ev-ery crea-ture's worth.
We will shel-ter safe-ly un-der-neath Your wing.
Your pure light re-veals how we are seen by You.

WORDS: Para. Psalms 36:5-9 Carol Reed-Jones
MUSIC: Carol Reed-Jones
Words and Music © 2017 The Christian Science Board of Directors

MEADOW COURT
12.11.11.11.

Love Divine, Your Healing Presence 529

1. Love di-vine, Your heal-ing pres-ence Lifts us to the ho-ly place,
2. Hum-ble hearts ac-cept Your bless-ing, Turn from sor-row, want, and sin.

Where we see Your whole cre-a-tion Filled with light and crowned with grace.
Turn the page, re-write that sto-ry, As the Christ is wel-comed in.

We Your chil-dren know your glo-ry, See Your pow-er from a-bove
Now we know our true re-la-tion, Per-fect God and per-fect child,

Sweep a-way the shade of dark-ness With the heal-ing tide of love.
We can live in joy and free-dom, Loved, and pure, and un-de-filed.

WORDS: Fenella Bennetts
MUSIC: William P. Rowlands

BLAENWERN
8.7.8.7.D.

530 Love Is Kind and Suffers Long

1. Love is kind and suf - fers long,
Love is meek and thinks no wrong,
Love than death it - self more strong;
There - fore give us love.

2. Proph - e - cy will fade a - way,
Melt - ing in the light of day;
Love will ev - er with us stay;
There - fore give us love.

3. Faith will van - ish in - to sight;
Hope shall be ful - filled in light;
Love will ev - er shine more bright;
There - fore give us love.

4. Faith and hope and love we see
Join - ing hand in hand a - gree;
But the great - est of the three,
And the best, is love.

I Corinthians 13:4, 8, 13.

WORDS: Christopher Wordsworth, adapt.
MUSIC: Nicholas P. Schliapin

LOVE IS KIND
7.7.7.5.
Alternate tune: 173

My One Desire, Dear Lord 531

1. My one de - sire, dear Lord, with You to walk; And
2. While in that sweet con - verse, as friend to friend, What
3. With - in that hal - lowed at - mo - sphere with You, My

in that sweet com - mu - nion, day by day,
bound - less love would You to me un - fold,
ev - ery thought with pur - est love im - bued,

So quick - ened be, that I may hear You talk, And
And truths re - veal, whose worth should far tran - scend Earth's
I would re - joice— to see Your vi - sion true— And

gar - ner close - ly all that You would say.
rar - est gems or price - less gifts of gold.
let my deeds at - test my grat - i - tude.

The words of this hymn are from a poem entitled "Desire" printed in the February 14, 1925 issue of the *Christian Science Sentinel*. The tune is by 17th-century composer Henry Lawes, considered to be the leading English songwriter of his day.

WORDS: E. Jewel Robinson, alt.
MUSIC: Henry Lawes, alt.

FARLEY CASTLE
10.10.10.10.

532 May God Give Us Her Blessing

Que Deus nos abençoe

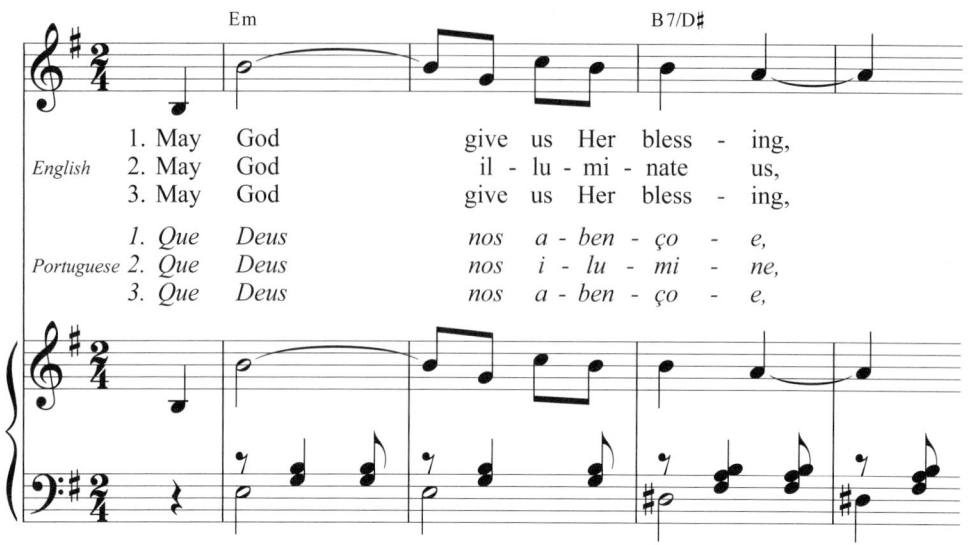

Numbers 6:24–26 / Psalms 119:105.

WORDS: Verse 1 para. Numbers 6:24–26; verses 2, 3 Leide Lessa; Eng. tr. CSPS
MUSIC: Dagmar P. R. Borges and Gelson Luíz

7.10.6.10.

Port. Words vss. 2, 3, Eng. tr. all vss. © 2017 The Christian Science Board of Directors
Music © 2000 Dagmar Borges and Gelson Luíz

533 My Life Flows on in Endless Song

1. My life flows on in end-less song A-bove earth's lam-en-ta-tion; I hear the sweet though far-off hymn That hails a new cre-a-tion. Through all the tu-mult and the strife I hear the mu-sic ring-ing; It

2. What though my hu-man com-forts die, The Lord my Sav-ior liv-eth; What though the dark-ness gath-er round, Songs in the night God giv-eth. No storm can shake my in-most calm While to that Rock I'm cling-ing; Since

3. I lift mine eyes, the cloud grows thin; I see the blue a-bove it. And day by day this path-way smooths Since first I learned to love it. The peace of Christ makes fresh my heart, A foun-tain ev-er spring-ing; All

Pastor at several Baptist churches in New York, New Jersey, and Philadelphia, Robert Lowry was an important compiler of hymns and composer of Sunday-school songs. Active in the second part of the 19th century, Lowry, a prominent figure in the nascent gospel hymn genre, composed many familiar tunes, including "I Need Thee Every Hour," and "Shall We Gather by the River?" This hymn was included in Lowry's 1869 collection *Bright Jewels for the Sunday School*.

WORDS: Pauline T., adapt., alt.
MUSIC: Robert Lowry; harm. Robert Rockabrand
Words adapt. and Music harm. © 2008 The Christian Science Board of Directors

ENDLESS SONG
8.7.8.7.D.

finds an ech - o in my soul. How can I keep from sing-ing?
Love is God of heaven and earth, How can I keep from sing-ing?
things are mine since I am God's. How can I keep from sing-ing?

534 My Shepherd Is the Living God

1. My shep-herd is the liv-ing God, There's noth-ing that I need;
2. When I walk through the shades of death, Your pres-ence is my stay;
3. The sure pro-vi-sions of my God At-tend me all my days;

In pas-tures fair, near pleas-ant streams, I set-tle down to feed.
A word of Your sup-port-ing breath Drives all my fears a-way.
O may Your house be my a-bode, And all my work be praise.

You bring my wan-dering spir-it back When I for-sake Your ways.
Your hand, in sight of all my foes, Lays out my ta-ble's spread;
There would I find a set-tled rest, While oth-ers come and go—

And lead me for Your mer-cy's sake In paths of truth and grace.
And fills my cup to o-ver-flow, Your oil a-noints my head.
No more a stran-ger or a guest, But like a child at home.

WORDS: Composite para. Psalm 23 Thomas Sternhold and Isaac Watts, alt.
MUSIC: American melody, Lewis's *Beauties of Harmony*, 1828; harm. Erik Routley
Music harm. © 1976 Hinshaw Music, Inc. (admin. Fred Bock Music Company, Inc.)

RESIGNATION
C.M.D.

My Sisters, Bless the Lord 535

1. My sis - ters, My sis - ters, bless the Lord,
2. My broth - ers, My broth - ers, bless the Lord,
3. All chil - dren, All chil - dren, bless the Lord,
4. To - geth - er, To - geth - er,

My sis - ters,
My broth - ers, bless the Lord, There is no oth - er God. God.
All chil - dren,
To - geth - er,

This hymn was originally sung in a responsorial manner: a leader initiates each phrase, with the group responding with the words "bless the Lord." If sung in this way, the leader enters with each new phrase while the group is holding the word "Lord," and then all sing "There is no other God."

WORDS: Anon. Kenya
MUSIC: Kenyan melody; arr. CSPS

6.6.6.6.

536 No Mortal Sense Can Still or Stay

1. No mor-tal sense can still or stay The
2. The heart's own long - ing lifts it high Where
3. The voic - es that are world - ly wise, With

flight of si - lent prayer, Un - ceas - ing, voice - less,
words can nev - er reach, Though hu - man lips may
mor - tal modes in tune, Are mute in that tran -

heart - de - sire That seeks God ev - ery - where.
nev - er form That glo - ry in - to speech.
scen - dent hour When God and man com - mune.

The words of this hymn are from a poem entitled "Silent Prayer," published in the July 1903 issue of *The Christian Science Journal*. This hymn tune, a traditional American melody, is called "Land of Rest" because it is associated with that text in B. F. White's *The Sacred Harp* (1844).

WORDS: Samuel Greenwood, alt.
MUSIC: American melody, Wakefield's *The Christian Harp*, 1836;
arr. Annabel Morris Buchanan; harm. Charles H. Webb

LAND OF REST
C.M.
Alternate tunes: 194, 410

O Church of God

537

1. O church of God, built on a firm foun - da - tion,
2. We hear the Word, in song and ser - mon spo - ken,
3. O Spir - it, feed us with Your bread from heav - en,
4. We feel Your peace, Your arms of Love en - fold - ing,

Stand - ing se - cure a - mid the storms of life,
In si - lent prayer, we turn to God to - day;
We drink Your liv - ing wa - ter and are free;
We lift our hearts in praise and grat - i - tude.

Where all may come to learn of true sal - va - tion
Our hum - ble hearts re - ceive the bless - ed to - ken
And ev - ery les - son that Your love has giv - en,
We, from this hour, a glimpse of heaven be - hold - ing,

And find re - lease from dis - cord, pain, and strife.
Of Truth that guides us in the up - ward way.
Oh, may we learn it with hu - mil - i - ty.
Go for - ward with our joy and strength re - newed.

Exodus 16:4, 15; 17:6 / Nehemiah 9:15 / Psalms 78:16, 21 / John 6:33, 58. The words of this hymn are from a poem entitled "Service in The Mother Church," first published in the October 8, 1955 issue of the *Christian Science Sentinel*.

WORDS: Ruby Nilson, alt.
MUSIC: William J. Reynolds

MORA PROCTOR
11.10.11.10.

538   O Come, All Ye Faithful

1. O come, all ye faith-ful, Joy-ful and tri-um-phant,
2. Sing, choirs of an-gels, Sing in ex-ul-ta-tion,
3. Yea, Lord, we greet thee, Born this hap-py morn-ing,

O come ye, O come ye, to Beth-le-hem.
Sing, all ye cit-i-zens of heaven a-bove.
Je-sus, to thee be all glo-ry given.

Come and be-hold him, born the King of An-gels;
Glo-ry to God, glo-ry in the high-est.
Word of the Fa-ther, now in flesh ap-pear-ing;

Unison

O come, let us a-dore him, O come, let us a-dore him,

Luke 2:13, 14. Attributed to John Francis Wade, who published the melody in the 18th century, this harmonization, which gained widespread acceptance in the 20th century, originated in *The English Hymnal* (1906), under the editorship of Ralph Vaughan Williams.

WORDS: Latin, 18th c.; tr. Frederick Oakeley and others
MUSIC: John Francis Wade; harm. *The English Hymnal*, 1906

ADESTE FIDELES
Irregular

Harmony

O come, let us a - dore him, Christ the Lord.

539   O Gentle Presence

"Mother's Evening Prayer" by Mary Baker Eddy

1. O gen - tle pres - ence, peace and joy and
2. Love is our ref - uge; on - ly with mine
3. O make me glad for ev - ery scald - ing
4. Be - neath the shad - ow of His might - y
5. No snare, no fowl - er, pes - ti - lence or

power;   O Life di - vine,   that
eye   Can I be - hold   the
tear,   For hope de - ferred,   in -
wing;   In that sweet se - cret
pain;   No night drops down   up -

WORDS: Mary Baker Eddy
MUSIC: Lisa Redfern; arr. CSPS

Music © 2010 The Christian Science Board of Directors
Music arr. © 2017 The Christian Science Board of Directors

SANDRA'S MELODY
10.10.10.10.
Alternate tunes: 207–212, 540

540 O Gentle Presence

"Mother's Evening Prayer" by Mary Baker Eddy

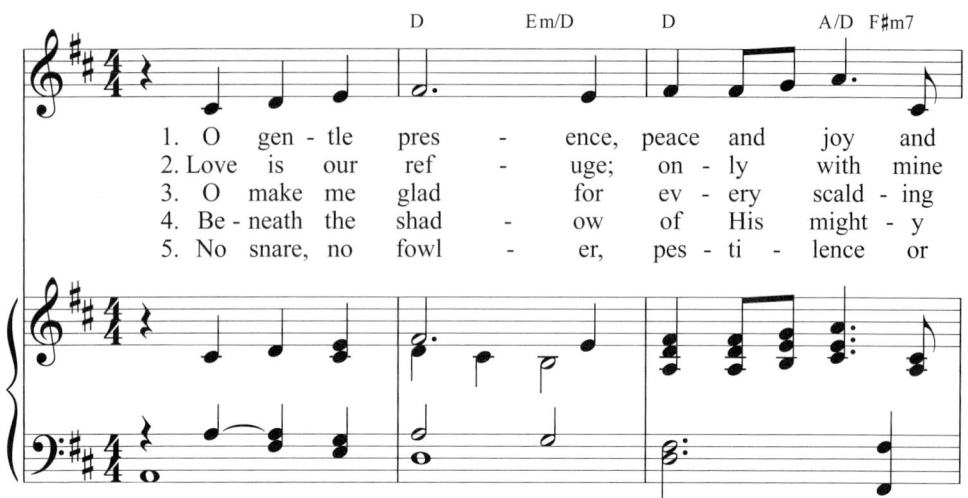

1. O gen - tle pres - ence, peace and joy and
2. Love is our ref - uge; on - ly with mine
3. O make me glad for ev - ery scald - ing
4. Be - neath the shad - ow of His might - y
5. No snare, no fowl - er, pes - ti - lence or

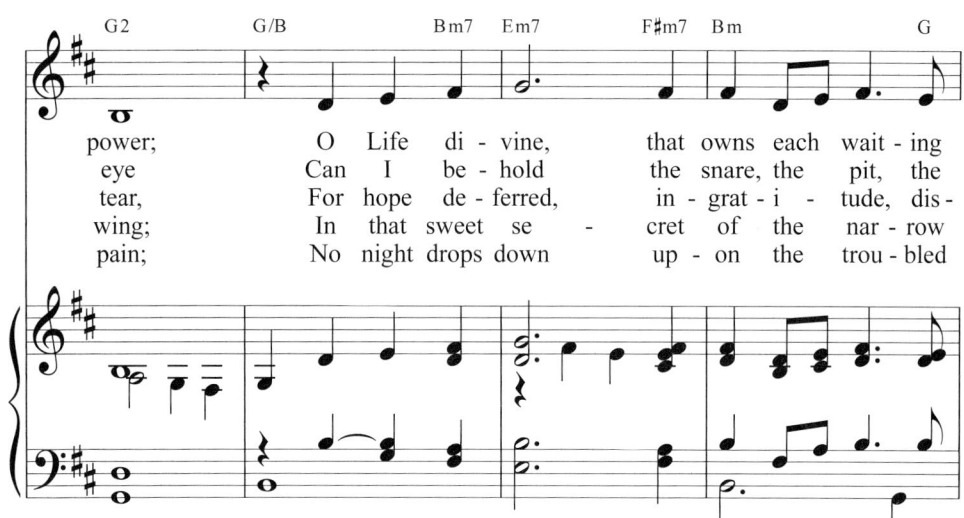

power;   O Life di - vine,   that owns each wait - ing
eye   Can I be - hold   the snare, the pit, the
tear,   For hope de - ferred,   in - grat - i - tude, dis -
wing;   In that sweet se - cret of the nar - row
pain;   No night drops down   up - on the trou - bled

WORDS: Mary Baker Eddy
MUSIC: Susan Booth Mack Snipes; harm. Peter Stevens and Rebecca Stevens;
   arr. Margaret Dorn, alt.

HALMONI
10.10.10.10.
Alternate tunes: 207–212, 539

541 O God, My Friend and Guardian

1. O God, my Friend and Guardian, In all my times of need
I yield me to Your guiding, And follow where You lead.
No shadows of the darkness Will dim the light You send,
And night becomes the morning By Your divine command.

2. Forever Father-Mother, Your children everywhere
Are cherished in Your loving, Your kind, Your perfect care.
All-knowing and all-seeing, All-powerful, divine—
I know Your ever-presence Is healing humankind.

3. You sent Your Son as Savior That joy and health increase;
Your justice and Your mercy Will give the world its peace.
And when I humbly listen, I know my Guide is wise;
The pathway may seem rugged, But heaven is its prize.

WORDS: Adrienne M. Tindall, alt.
MUSIC: Welsh melody, Parry's *The Welsh Harper*, vol. 2, 1848; harm. David Evans

LLANGLOFFAN
7.6.7.6.D.

O Life That Maketh All Things New 542

1. O Life that mak - eth all things new, The bloom-ing
2. From hand to hand the greet-ing flows, From eye to
3. One in the free - dom of the truth, One in the
4. The fre - er step, the full - er breath, The wide ho-

earth, the thoughts of men; Our pil-grim feet, wet with Your
eye the sig - nals run, From heart to heart the bright hope
joy of paths un-trod, One in the heart's pe - ren - nial
ri - zon's grand - er view; The sense of Life that knows no

dew, In glad-ness hith - er turn a - gain.
glows, The seek - ers of the Light are one:
youth, One in the larg - er thought of God;—
death,— The Life that mak - eth all things new.

WORDS: Samuel Longfellow, alt.
MUSIC: Andrew D. Brewis, alt.
Music © 2008 Andrew D. Brewis

NEWSONG
L.M.
Alternate tunes: 218-220

543   O Jesus, Our Dear Master

1. O Jesus, our dear Master, Your works, now understood,
2. The Christ, eternal manhood, As God's own Son beloved,
3. O Science, God-sent message To tired humanity,

Reveal their full effulgence Through love and brotherhood.
A tender ever-presence Within each heart is proved.
You are Love's revelation Of Truth that makes us free.

Today Christ's precious Science Your healing power makes plain:
O God, our Father-Mother, Your name we see expressed
Your kingdom, God, within us Shows forth Love's sweet control.

Luke 17:21 / John 8:32.

WORDS: Margaret Glenn Matters, alt.
MUSIC: James R. Corbett

SWEET CONTROL
7.6.7.6.D.
Alternate tune: 221

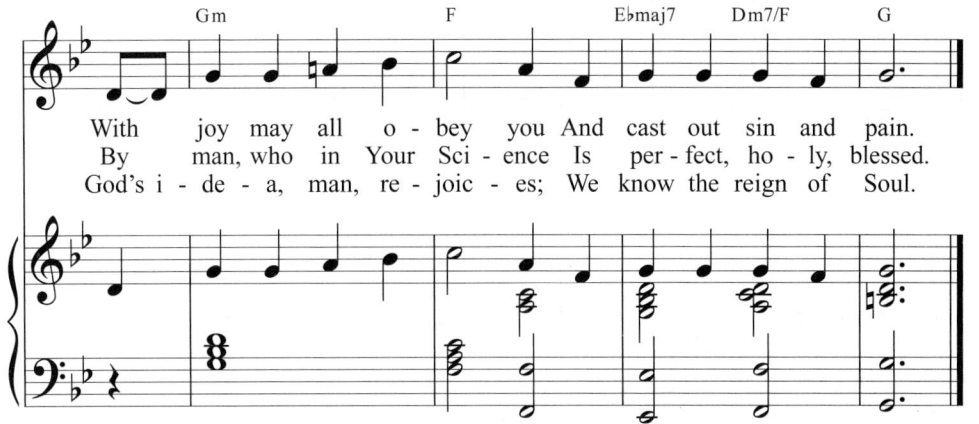

With   joy may all   o - bey   you And cast out sin and   pain.
By   man, who in Your Sci - ence Is   per - fect, ho - ly, blessed.
God's i - de - a, man, re - joic - es; We know the reign of   Soul.

544   O Little Town of Bethlehem

1. O lit-tle town of Beth-le-hem, How still we see thee lie;
   A-bove thy deep and dream-less sleep The si-lent stars go by;
   Yet in thy dark streets shin - eth The ev-er-last-ing Light;
   The hopes and fears of all the years Are met in thee to - night.

2. O morn-ing stars, to-geth - er Pro-claim the ho-ly birth,
   And prais-es sing to God the King, And peace to all on earth;
   Where char-i-ty stands watch - ing And faith holds wide the door,
   The dark night wakes, the glo - ry breaks, And Christ-mas comes once more.

3. How si-lent-ly, how si-lent-ly, The won-drous gift is given;
   So God im-parts to hu - man hearts The bless-ings of His heaven.
   No ear may hear his com - ing, But in this world of sin,
   Where meek-ness will re - ceive him, still The dear Christ en - ters in.

Luke 2:13, 14. This text, written by American Episcopal clergyman Phillips Brooks in 1868, was initially set to music by Lewis Redner—a pairing that remains popular to this day. The words were joined with the tune given here in *The English Hymnal* (1906), under the editorship of Ralph Vaughan Williams; in this form it is well known in the United Kingdom and parts of the world where the influence of the Anglican church is or has been particularly strong.

WORDS: Phillips Brooks, alt.
MUSIC: English melody; adapt. and harm. Ralph Vaughan Williams
Music arr. (in the UK) © 1906 Oxford University Press

FOREST GREEN
8.6.8.6.7.6.8.6.
Alternate tunes: 222, 223

O Sweet and Tender as the Dawn 545

1. O sweet and ten-der as the dawn, With might-y power to heal and bless, Is God's dear gift to all His own: The hap-py grace of gen-tle-ness.

2. How quick-ly bur-dens fall a-way, How hearts grow light, re-joice, are glad, When Love with touch of gen-tle-ness Up-lifts the sin-ning and the sad.

3. This gen-tle grace of Love di-vine Is sweet as breath of o-pening flower. Self-love and harsh-ness dis-ap-pear Be-neath its ten-der, heal-ing power.

WORDS: Ella A. Stone, alt.
MUSIC: Marshall Wright

FLEURETTE
L.M.
Alternate tunes: 243, 244

546 O Master, Let Me Walk with Thee

1. O Mas- ter, let me walk with thee In low- ly
3. Teach me your pa - tience; still with thee In clos - er,

paths of ser - vice free; Tell me your se - cret;
dear - er com - pa - ny, In work that keeps faith

help me bear The strain of toil, the fret of care.
sweet and strong, In trust that tri - umphs o - ver wrong.

This music is an arrangement of an organ chorale by Flor Peeters, a Belgian composer, organist, and teacher. Published in 1955, the work is indicative of Peeters's interest in contrapuntal techniques, and clear, balanced, classical forms.

WORDS: Washington Gladden, alt.
MUSIC: Flor Peeters; transc. and adapt. CSPS

Music © 1955, ren. 1983 The H. W. Gray Company (admin. Belwin-Mills Publishing Corp.)

NO. 37 CHORALE
L.M.
Alternate tunes: 234, 235

2. Help me the slow of heart to move By some clear
4. In hope that sends a shin - ing ray Far down the

win - ning word of love; Teach me the way - ward
fu - ture's broad - ening way; In peace that God a -

feet to stay, And guide them in the home - ward way.
lone can give, With you, O Mas - ter, let me live.

547 O, Sometimes Gleams upon Our Sight

1. O, sometimes gleams upon our sight, Through
2. For all of good the past has had Re-
4. Henceforth my heart shall sigh no more For

present wrong, th'eternal right; And step by step, since
mains to make our own time glad, Our common, daily
olden time and holier shore: God's love and blessing,

end here

time began, We see the steady gain of man.
life divine, And every land a Palestine. *to verse 3*
then and there, Are now and here and everywhere.

WORDS: John Greenleaf Whittier, alt.
MUSIC: Peter B. Allen
Music © 2008 Peter B. Allen

SHERWOOD
L.M.
Alternate tunes: 238, 239

3. Through the harsh nois - es of our day, A
low sweet pre - lude finds its way; Through clouds of doubt and
creeds of fear A light is break - ing, calm and clear.

to beginning

548   O Tender, Loving Shepherd

1. O ten-der, lov-ing Shep-herd, We long to fol-low thee,
2. We know, be-lov-ed Shep-herd, The path that you have trod
3. Through-out the way, dear Shep-herd, Your strong hand does up-hold;

To fol-low where you lead us, Though rough the path may be;
Leads ev-er out of dark-ness, And on and up to God.
The wea-ry ones, at night-fall, You gent-ly will en-fold.

Though dark and heav-y shad-ows En-shroud the way with gloom,
If from that path we wan-der, And far a-stray we roam,
And when to Truth's green pas-tures With joy at length we come,

We know that Love will guide us, And safe-ly lead us home.
O, call us, faith-ful Shep-herd, And bring us safe-ly home.
There shall we find, O Shep-herd, Our blest, e-ter-nal home.

WORDS: Frederic W. Root, alt.
MUSIC: Randall S. Updegraff; harm. CSPS

TENDER SHEPHERD
7.6.7.6.D.
Alternate tune: 245

O Thou Joyful
O du fröhliche

549

English O thou joy - ful, O thou bless - ed,
German O du fröh - li - che, o du se - li - ge,

O thou grace - bring - ing Christ - mas - tide!
gna - den - brin - gen - de Weih - nachts - zeit!

1. Cha - os and dark - ness yield to the Christ light.
2. Christ came to earth to show our at - one - ment.
3. Heav - en - ly hosts re - joice and em - brace us.

1. Welt ging ver - lo - ren, Christ ist ge - bo - ren:
2. Christ ist er - schie - nen, uns zu ver - suh - nen:
3. Himm - li - sche Hee - re jauch - zen Dir Eh - re:

Chris - tians sing with joy, in love a - bide.
Freu - e, freu - e dich, o Chris - ten - heit!

John 1:17 / Romans 5:11 / Acts 15:11. German writer and philanthropist Johann Daniel Falk wrote the words to
"O du fröhliche" in 1816, and included the hymn in his *Auserlesene Werke* (*Selected Works*, 1819); the version that
has become established as a popular Christmas hymn joins two new verses by Heinrich Holzschuher to Falk's
original first verse.

WORDS: Verse 1 Johann Daniel Falk; verses 2, 3 Heinrich Holzschuher; Eng. tr. CSPS
MUSIC: Sicilian melody; harm. Timothy Kirk Thomas

SICILY
10.8.10.9.
Alternate arr.: 119

Eng. tr. © 2015 The Christian Science Board of Directors
Eng. tr. alt. © 2017 The Christian Science Board of Directors
Music harm. © 1996 Gerth Medien Musikverlag

550 O'er Waiting Harpstrings

"Christ My Refuge" by Mary Baker Eddy

1. O'er wait - ing harp-strings of the mind There sweeps a strain,
3. Then His un-veiled, sweet mer - cies show Life's bur - dens light.
6. From tir - ed joy and grief a - far, And near - er Thee,—

Low, sad, and sweet, whose mea - sures bind The power of pain,
I kiss the cross, and wake to know A world more bright.
Fa - ther, where Thine own chil - dren are, I love to be.

2. And wake a white-winged an - gel throng Of thoughts, il - lumed
4. And o'er earth's trou - bled, an - gry sea I see Christ walk,
7. My prayer, some dai - ly good to do To Thine, for Thee;

end here

By faith, and breathed in rap - tured song, With love per - fumed.
And come to me, and ten - der - ly, Di - vine - ly talk.
An of - fering pure of Love, where-to God lead - eth me.

WORDS: Mary Baker Eddy
MUSIC: French melody, Arbeau's *Orchesographie*, 1589; harm. Robert Rockabrand
Music harm. © 2017 The Christian Science Board of Directors

ARBEAU
8.4.8.4.
Alternate tunes: 253–257, 551, 552

5. Thus Truth en-grounds me on the rock, Up - on Life's shore,

to beginning

'Gainst which the winds and waves can shock, Oh, nev - er - more!

551 O'er Waiting Harpstrings

"Christian My Refuge" by Mary Baker Eddy

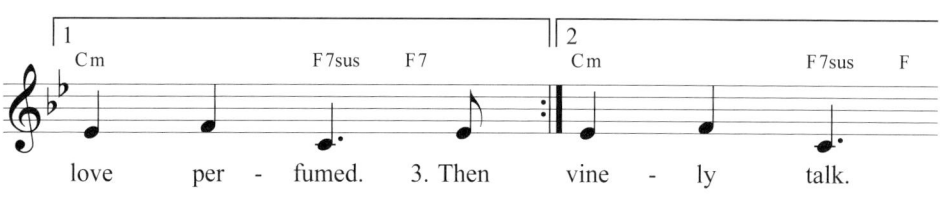

Bb / Bbmaj7 / Ebmaj7 F / Gm7

1. O'er wait-ing harp-strings of the mind There sweeps a strain,
(3.) His un-veiled, sweet mer-cies show Life's bur-dens light.

Cm7/G Bb / Bbmaj7 / Ebmaj7 F / Gm7 Eb

Low, sad, and sweet, whose mea-sures bind The power of pain,
I kiss the cross, and wake to know A world more bright.

Eb Gm7 / C / F / Bb F/A Eb/G

2. And wake a white-winged an-gel throng Of thoughts, il-lumed
4. And o'er earth's trou-bled, an-gry sea I see Christ walk,

Cm/G Eb / Bb

By faith, and breathed in rap-tured song, With
And come to me, and ten-der-ly, Di -

[1]
Cm / F7sus F7

love per-fumed. 3. Then

[2]
Cm / F7sus F

vine-ly talk.

F Eb / Fsus / Gm / Bb / F/Bb Bb

5. Thus Truth en-grounds me on the rock, Up-on Life's shore,

WORDS: Mary Baker Eddy
MUSIC: Cherie Brennan
Music © 2017 The Christian Science Board of Directors

HEART SONG
8.4.8.4.
Alternate tunes: 253–257, 550, 552

'Gainst which the winds and waves can shock, Oh, nev-er-more!

6. From tired joy and grief a-far, And near-er Thee,—

Fa-ther, where Thine own chil-dren are, I love to be.

7. My prayer, some dai-ly good to do To Thine, for Thee;

An of-fering pure of Love, where-to God lead-eth me.

552 O'er Waiting Harpstrings

"Christ My Refuge" by Mary Baker Eddy

1. O'er wait-ing harp-strings of the mind There sweeps a strain,
3. Then His un-veiled, sweet mer-cies show Life's bur-dens light.
6. From tir-ed joy and grief a-far, And near-er Thee,—

Low, sad, and sweet, whose mea-sures bind The power of pain,
I kiss the cross, and wake to know A world more bright.
Fa-ther, where Thine own chil-dren are, I love to be.

2. And wake a white-winged an-gel throng Of thoughts, il-lumed By
4. And o'er earth's trou-bled, an-gry sea I see Christ walk, And
7. My prayer, some dai-ly good to do To Thine, for Thee; An

Last time to ✠ Coda

1
faith, and breathed in rap-tured song, With love per-fumed.
come to me, and
of-fering pure of

2
ten-der-ly, Di-

vine-ly talk. 5. Thus Truth en-grounds me on the rock, Up-on Life's

to beginning

shore, 'Gainst which the winds and waves can shock, Oh, nev-er-more!

✠ Coda

Love, where-to God lead-eth me.

WORDS: Mary Baker Eddy
MUSIC: Peter B. Allen
Music © 2016 The Christian Science Board of Directors

HARPSTRINGS
8.4.8.4.
Alternate tunes: 253–257, 550, 551

Our Desire to Heed God's Calling 553

1. Our de-sire to heed God's call-ing Lifts us
2. When our own plans seem to crum-ble In - com-
3. With the mod - el right be - fore us, Per - fect
4. Far be - yond the bounds of mat - ter, Un - re -

to a new de - sign, Out - lined by pure
plete or ill - de - fined, Let us turn to
God and per - fect man, Let God's whole-ness
strained by fear or time, All our plans un -

in - spi - ra - tion, Ren - dered in Love's grace - ful line.
God's cre - a - tion, Al - ways per - fect-ly a - ligned.
reign with - in us, Let Mind's will per - fect our plan.
fold to - geth-er In Soul's har - mo - ny and rhyme.

This tune was first published in Amos Pilsbury's *United States' Sacred Harmony* (1799), an important collection of hymn tunes that strongly influenced the development of American hymnody in the 19th century. Originally setting the words "Come, Thou Fount of Every Blessing," this tune appeared in six hymnals over the next 50 years, including *Western Harmony* (1824), where the name of the tune was changed from "Charleston" to "Charlestown."

WORDS: Mara Purl, alt.
MUSIC: American melody, Pilsbury's *United States' Sacred Harmony*, 1799; arr. CSPS

CHARLESTOWN
8.7.8.7.

554

One by One

1. One by one, pure thoughts and ho - ly Lift us
2. One by one, our aims grow pur - er, As our
3. Then with - in Love's ev - er - pres - ence We shall

out of self and sin; One by one, bright gleams of
deeds re - flect our God; One by one, our path grows
live a - mid its light, Know-ing well that ho - ly

glo - ry Show the goal we all will win. One by
clear - er, Guid - ed by Love's staff and rod. One by
bril - liance Which is called the In - fi - nite. Know the

one, our trusts are strength - ened, As our
one, our thoughts move for - ward To the
glo - ries of God's king - dom, Hear the

Psalms 23:4 / John 10:16 / Acts 17:28. The words of this hymn first appeared as a poem in the January 1902 issue of *The Christian Science Journal.*

WORDS: Carol Norton, alt.
MUSIC: W. Irving Hartshorn
Words alt. © 2016 The Christian Science Board of Directors

IRVING
8.7.8.7.D.

Eb   Cm7   F7   Bb   Eb   Bb   Eb

lives   to   God   we   give;   One   by   one,   our   days   are
time   by   proph - ets   told;   One   by   one,   our   lives move
mu - sic Spir - it   sings, Be   at   one   with that   great

Eb   Ab   Eb/Bb   Bb7   Eb

length - ened, While   in   Love   we   move   and   live.
home - ward   Sing - ing   of   one   Lord,   one   fold.
Wis - dom   From   which   all   cre - a   -   tion   springs.

555

Only Love
El amor

English
1. On - ly love, on - ly love, Suf - fers
2. On - ly love, on - ly love, Thinks of

Spanish
1. El a - mor, el a - mor, es pa -
2. El a - mor, el a - mor, nun - ca

long and sac - ri - fi - ces all. Love helps us each to live gra - cious-
oth - ers, not just of it - self, Re - joic - es not in wrong but in

cien - te y ple - no de bon - dad. Él nun - ca de - ja - rá de e - xis -
pien - sa só - lo pa - ra sí; se a - fir - ma siem - pre en la Ver -

I Corinthians 13. This hymn is based upon a song from Rafael Grullón's oratorio, *El caminante de Nazaret* (The Walker from Nazareth).

WORDS: Rafael Grullón, adapt.; Eng. tr. S T Kimbrough Jr., adapt.
MUSIC: Rafael Grullón; arr. Jorge Lockward, adapt.
Words and Music © 1987 Abingdon Press (admin. Music Services)

GRULLÓN
6.9.9.13.7.9.

556 Our Father Knows My Need Today

1. Our Father knows my need to-day; I do not mere-ly ask For hap-py hours or gold-en way, Or lov-ing, help-ful task;

2. Our Father knows my need this hour; Wher-e'er my steps may go, The sav-ing light from Truth's high tower, Now leads me— this I know.

3. Our Moth-er knows this mo-ment's need,— My work, my prayer, my song, The heal-ing word and Christ-like deed. Here where the way seems long,

4. Love sets the earth-bound cap-tive free; And, mind-ful of Her own, With lov-ing care God's lead-ing me. When wan-der-ing and lone,

Exodus 16:15 / Hebrews 10:20. The words to this hymn are from a poem entitled "Confidence," first published in the February 1907 issue of *The Christian Science Journal*.

WORDS: Agnes Chalmers, alt.
MUSIC: Raymond David Burkhart

OMNISCIENCE
8.6.8.6.8.8.

Music © 2016 The Christian Science Board of Directors

But, with all trust in Love, I pray: Our
Yours is the maj - es - ty and power, O
Truth's man - na falls and I am fed; Love's
I find in Truth the liv - ing way: Our

Fa - ther knows my need to - day.
Love di - vine, this day— this hour.
light shines clear and I am led.
Moth - er knows my need to - day.

557 Our Father-Mother, Your Will Be Done

Mayenziwe 'ntando yakho

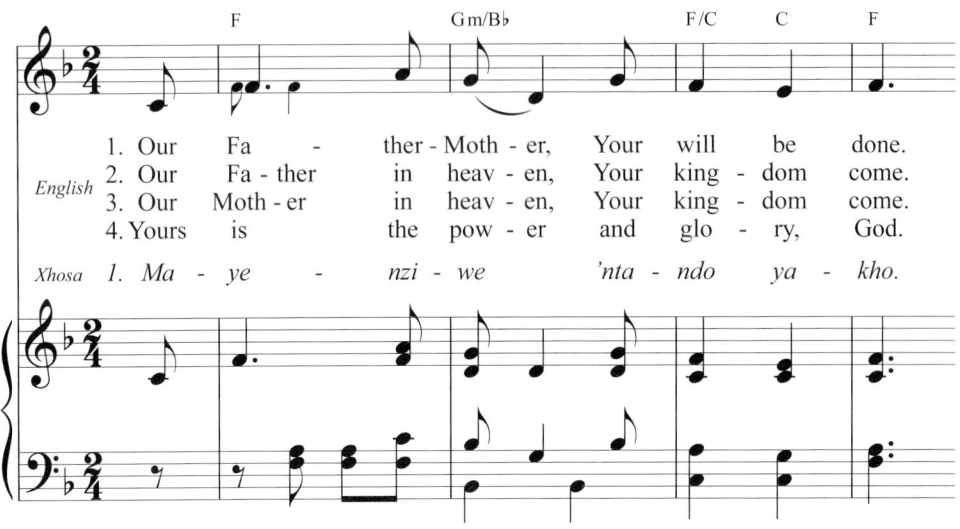

English
1. Our Fa - ther - Moth - er, Your will be done.
2. Our Fa - ther in heav - en, Your king - dom come.
3. Our Moth - er in heav - en, Your king - dom come.
4. Yours is the pow - er and glo - ry, God.

Xhosa 1. Ma - ye - nzi - we 'nta - ndo ya - kho.

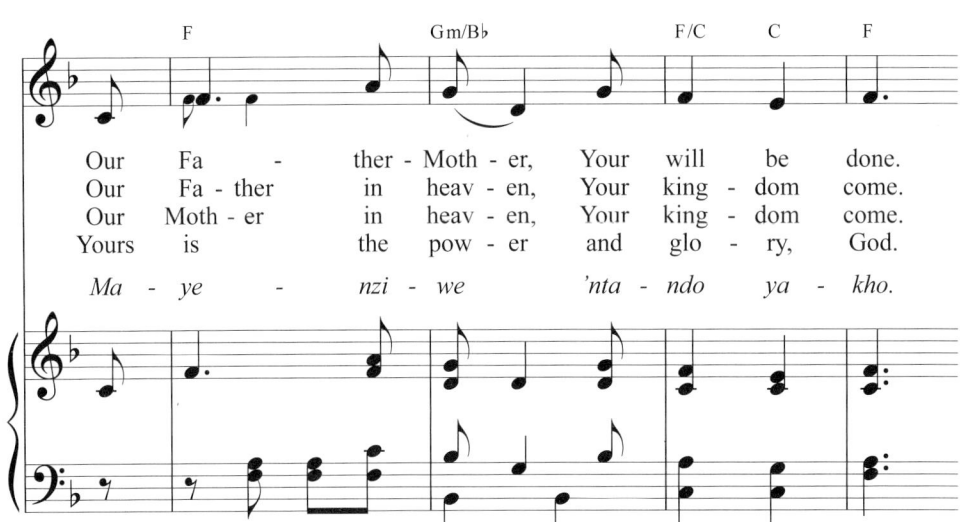

Our Fa - ther - Moth - er, Your will be done.
Our Fa - ther in heav - en, Your king - dom come.
Our Moth - er in heav - en, Your king - dom come.
Yours is the pow - er and glo - ry, God.

Ma - ye - nzi - we 'nta - ndo ya - kho.

Matthew 6:9–13.

WORDS: Verse 1 anon. South Africa; Eng. tr., adapt., and additional verses CSPS
MUSIC: South African melody, as taught by George A. Mxadana;
arr. General Board of Global Ministries, GBGMusik, alt.

Irregular

558 Our Father Which Art in Heaven

The Lord's Prayer

Our Fa-ther which art in heav-en, Hal-low-ed be Thy name.

Thy king-dom come. Thy will be done in earth, as it is in heaven.

Give us this day our dai-ly bread; And for-give us our debts, as

WORDS: Matthew 6:9–13
MUSIC: Ryan Vigil
Music © 2017 The Christian Science Board of Directors

PRAYER
Irregular
Alternate tune: 559

we for-give our debt-ors. And lead us not in-to temp-ta - tion, But de-

liv - er us from e - vil: For Thine is the king-dom, and the

pow-er, and the glo - ry, for - ev - er. A - men.

559 Our Father Which Art in Heaven

The Lord's Prayer

WORDS: Matthew 6:9–13
MUSIC: Wendy Wylie Winegar; arr. Randall Woltz
Music © 2016 The Christian Science Board of Directors

ASPIRATION
Irregular
Alternate tune: 558

Our God Shall Reign

560

1. Our God shall reign wher-e'er the sun Does its suc-
2. All peo-ple shall with joy-ful tongue Dwell on God's
3. For bless-ings flow wher-e'er You reign; The pris-oner
4. Let ev-ery crea-ture rise and bring Their gifts of

ces - sive jour - neys run; God's truth shall stretch from
love with sweet - est song, And in - fant voic - es
leaps to loose his chains, The wea - ry find e -
praise for all to sing; Let an - gel songs be

shore to shore, Till moons shall wax and wane no more.
shall pro - claim Their ear - ly bless - ings on Your name.
ter - nal rest, And ev - ery child on earth is blessed.
heard a - gain And earth re - peat the long A - men.

This music is based upon a traditional Korean melody; besides the current arrangement, this hymn can be performed a capella, or with instruments doubling the melody line.

WORDS: Isaac Watts, adapt., alt.
MUSIC: Korean melody; arr. CSPS

DORAJI
L.M.
Alternate tunes: 271, 272

561 Our Heavenly Father-
Mother Love Abiding

1. Our heaven-ly Fa - ther - Moth-er Love a - bid-ing,
2. O give us grace to meet the com-ing mor-row;

We wor-ship You, We praise Your ho - ly name.
For - give our debts as oth-ers we for - give.

Teach us Your chil - dren ev - er-more to love You;
You nev - er lead Your chil-dren to temp - ta - tion.

This text, based upon the Lord's Prayer, is joined here with the well-known tune from Jean Sibelius's 1900 orchestral work *Finlandia*.

WORDS: Para. Matthew 6:9–13 Richard D. Row, alt.
MUSIC: Jean Sibelius; arr. Richard D. Row, alt.
Words and Music arr. © 1947, ren. 1975 R. D. Row Music Co., Inc. (admin. Carl Fischer, LLC)

FINLANDIA
11.10.11.10.11.10.
Alternate arr.: 469

Your will be done in earth as heaven to - day.
De - liv - er us from e - vil and from sin.

Teach us Your chil - dren ev - er - more to love You;
Yours is the king - dom, Yours the power and glo - ry,

Your will be done in earth as heaven to - day.
World with - out end, for - ev - er - more, A - men.

Praise, I Will Praise You, Lord 562

Je louerai l'Eternel

English
1. Praise, I will praise You, Lord, with all my heart. O
2. Love, I will love You, Lord, with all my heart. O
3. Serve, I will serve You, Lord, with all my heart. O

French
1. Je loue - rai l'E - ter - nel de tout mon cœur, Je

God, I will tell the won-ders of Your ways, And glo - ri - fy Your name.
ra - con - te - rai tou - tes Tes mer-veilles, Je chan - te - rai Ton nom.

Praise, I will praise You, Lord, with all my heart. In
Love, I will love You, Lord, with all my heart. In
Serve, I will serve You, Lord, with all my heart. In
Je loue - rai l'E - ter - nel de tout mon cœur, Je

You I will find the source of all my joy. Al - le - lu - ia!
fe - rai de Toi le su - jet de ma joie. Al - lé - lu - ia!

French: 2. J'aimerai l'Eternel... 3. Je suivrai l'Eternel...

WORDS: Para. Psalms 9:1, 2 Claude Fraysée; Eng. tr. Kenneth I. Morse
MUSIC: Claude Fraysée; harm. Alain Bergèse

10.11.6.10.11.4.

563 Quiet, Lord, My Stubborn Heart

1. Qui-et, Lord, my stub-born heart, Make me gen-tle, pure, and mild,
2. What You shall to-day pro-vide Let me as a child re-ceive,
3. As a lit-tle child re-lies On a care be-yond its own,

Up-right, sim-ple, free from art; Make me as a lit-tle child,
What to-mor-row may be-tide Calm-ly to Your wis-dom leave;
Be-ing nei-ther strong nor wise, Will not take a step a-lone,

From dis-trust and en-vy free, Pleased with all that pleas-es Thee.
It's e-nough that You will care, Why should I the bur-den bear?
Let me thus with You a-bide, As my Moth-er, Friend, and Guide.

WORDS: John Newton, adapt., alt.
MUSIC: Pontoppidan's *Den Nye Psalme-Bog*, 1740; harm. CSPS
Words adapt. © 1932, ren. 1960 The Christian Science Board of Directors
Music harm. © 2017 The Christian Science Board of Directors

STILLE ER MIN SIEL TIL GUD
7.7.7.7.7.7.
Alternate tunes: 291, 564

Quiet, Lord, My Stubborn Heart 564

1. Qui - et, Lord, my stub-born heart, Make me gen-tle, pure, and mild,
2. What You shall to - day pro - vide Let me as a child re - ceive,
3. As a lit - tle child re - lies On a care be-yond its own,

Up-right, sim - ple, free from art; Make me as a lit - tle child,
What to - mor - row may be - tide Calm - ly to Your wis-dom leave;
Be - ing nei - ther strong nor wise, Will not take a step a - lone,

From dis-trust and en - vy free, Pleased with all that pleas - es Thee.
It's e-nough that You will care, Why should I the bur - den bear?
Let me thus with You a - bide, As my Moth-er, Friend, and Guide.

WORDS: John Newton, adapt., alt.
MUSIC: Fenella Bennetts

RIPLEY
7.7.7.7.7.7.
Alternate tunes: 291, 563

Words adapt. © 1932, ren. 1960 The Christian Science Board of Directors
Music © 2016 The Christian Science Board of Directors

565 Rise Up and Walk

1. Rise up and walk, take up your bed. With these few words the
2. Cleanse the lep - ers, heal the sick. Cast out de - mons.

sick - ness fled. Stretch forth your hand. Re - ceive your sight.
Raise the dead. Truth is re - vealed in ev - ery place,

Je - sus' com - mands re - veal God's might. You are God's pur - pose,
Through-out all time, through-out all space. Right in this mo - ment,

His great de - sign. Beau - ti - ful, blame - less,
do - ing God's will "These works shall you do,

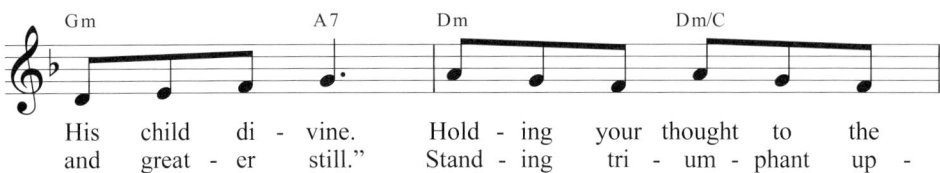

His child di - vine. Hold - ing your thought to the
and great - er still." Stand - ing tri - um - phant up -

good and the true, Spir - it will form you a - new.
on ho - ly ground, Songs of the an - gels re - sound.

Isaiah 44:23; 55:12 / Matthew 10:8; 12:13 / Mark 3:5 / Luke 5:23, 24; 18:42 / John 5:8; 14:12. The second verse of
this hymn quotes the words—drawn from the American Standard translation of the Bible—encircling the Cross and
Crown trademark that identifies the authorized writings of Mary Baker Eddy.

WORDS and MUSIC: Peter B. Allen
Words and Music © 2008 Peter B. Allen

RISE UP
Irregular

Refrain

Rise up and walk! God made you free, Born of His lib - er -

ty. Care - free and strong, you are His song,

Per - fect for all to see. Moun - tains and seas,

great ris - ing trees, Ech - o the joy - ous song:

Heav - en is here, har - mo - ny's bliss To ev - ery - one be -

1. longs.

2. longs.

566   Rock of Ages

1. Rock of Ages, Truth divine,
Be Thy strength forever mine;
Let me rest secure on Thee,

2. Rock of Truth, our fortress strong,
Thou our refuge from all wrong,
When from mortal sense I flee,

3. Christ, the Truth, foundation sure,
On this rock we are secure;
Peace is there our life to fill,

Psalms 62:7.

WORDS: Frederic W. Root, based on a hymn by A. M. Toplady
MUSIC: James H. Hegarty

STRENGTH ABIDING
7.7.7.7.7.7.
Alternate tunes: 293–295, 567

567 Rock of Ages

1. Rock of Ages, Truth divine,
   Be Thou strength forever mine;
   Let me rest secure on Thee,
   Safe above life's raging sea.

2. Rock of Truth, our fortress strong,
   Thou our refuge from all wrong,
   When from mortal sense I flee,
   Let me hide myself in Thee.

3. Christ, the Truth, foundation sure,
   On this rock we are secure;
   Peace is there our life to fill,
   Cure is there for every ill.

Rock of Ages,

Psalms 62:7.

WORDS: Frederic W. Root, based on a hymn by A. M. Toplady
MUSIC: Raymond David Burkhart

EAGLE ROCK
7.7.7.7.7.7.
Alternate tunes: 293–295, 566

Truth di - vine, Be Thy strength for - ev - er mine.

568

Saw Ye My Saviour?

"Communion Hymn" by Mary Baker Eddy

1. Saw ye my Sav - iour? Heard ye the glad sound? Felt ye the
2. Mourn - er, it calls you,— "Come to my bos - om, Love wipes your
3. Sin - ner, it calls you,— "Come to this foun - tain, Cleanse the foul
4. Strong-est de - liv - erer, friend of the friend - less, Life of all

pow - er of the Word? 'Twas the Truth that made us free, And was
tears all a - way, And will lift the shade of gloom, And for
sens - es with - in; 'Tis the Spir - it that makes pure, That ex-
be - ing di - vine: Thou the Christ, and not the creed; Thou the

found by you and me In the life and the love of our Lord.
you make ra - diant room Midst the glo - ries of one end-less day."
alts thee, and will cure All thy sor - row and sick-ness and sin."
Truth in thought and deed; Thou the wa - ter, the bread, and the wine.

WORDS: Mary Baker Eddy
MUSIC: Dimasa Piatu
Music © 2016 The Christian Science Board of Directors

TENDRESSE
10.7.7.7.9.
Alternate tunes: 298–302, 569–571

Saw Ye My Saviour?

"Communion Hymn" by Mary Baker Eddy

569

1. Saw ye my Sav-iour? Heard ye the glad sound?
2. Mourn-er, it calls you,— "Come to my bos-om,
4. Strong-est de-liv-er-er, friend of the friend-less,

Felt ye the pow-er of the Word? 'Twas the
Love wipes your tears all a-way, And will
Life of all be-ing di-vine: Thou the

Truth that made us free, And was found by you and
lift the shade of gloom, And for you make ra-diant
Christ, and not the creed; Thou the Truth in thought and

me In the life and the love of our Lord.
room Midst the glo-ries of one end-less day." *to verse 3*
deed; Thou the wa-ter, the bread, and the wine.

end here

3. Sin-ner, it calls you,— "Come to this foun-tain, Cleanse the foul

sens-es with-in; 'Tis the Spir-it that makes pure, That ex-

to verse 4

alts thee, and will cure All thy sor-row and sick-ness and sin."

WORDS: Mary Baker Eddy
MUSIC: Désirée Goyette
Music © 2008 The Christian Science Board of Directors

LINCOLN
10.7.7.7.9.
Alternate tunes: 298–302, 568, 570, 571

570 Saw Ye My Saviour?

"Communion Hymn" by Mary Baker Eddy

1. Saw ye my Saviour? Heard ye the glad sound? Felt ye the power of the Word? 'Twas the Truth that made us free, And was

2. Mourner, it calls you,— "Come to my bosom, Love wipes your tears all away, And will lift the shade of gloom, And for

3. Sinner, it calls you,— "Come to this fountain, Cleanse the foul senses within; 'Tis the Spirit that makes pure, That ex-

4. Strongest deliverer, friend of the friendless, Life of all being divine: Thou the Christ, and not the creed; Thou the

WORDS: Mary Baker Eddy
MUSIC: Natsumi Malloy
Music © 2017 The Christian Science Board of Directors

REIMEI
10.7.7.7.9.
Alternate tunes: 298–302, 568, 569, 571

found   by   you   and   me   In   the
you   make   ra - diant   room   Midst   the
alts   thee, and   will   cure   All   thy
Truth   in thought   and   deed;   Thou   the

life   and   the   love   of   our   Lord.
glo - ries   of   one   end - less   day."
sor - row   and   sick - ness and   sin."
wa - ter,   the   bread,   and   the   wine.

571 Saw Ye My Saviour?

"Communion Hymn" by Mary Baker Eddy

1. Saw ye my Sav - iour? Heard ye the glad sound? Felt ye the power of the Word? 'Twas the Truth that made us free, And was found by you and me In the life and the love of our Lord.

2. Mourn - er, it calls you,— "Come to my bos - om, Love wipes your tears all a - way, And will lift the shade of gloom, And for you make ra - diant room Midst the glo - ries of one end - less day."

3. Sin - ner, it calls you,— "Come to this foun - tain, Cleanse the foul sens - es with - in; 'Tis the Spir - it that makes pure, That ex - alts thee, and will cure All thy sor - row and sick - ness and sin."

4. Strong - est de - liv - erer, friend of the friend - less, Life of all be - ing di - vine: Thou the Christ, and not the creed; Thou the Truth in thought and deed; Thou the wa - ter, the bread, and the wine.

WORDS: Mary Baker Eddy
MUSIC: Fenella Bennetts
Music © 2016 The Christian Science Board of Directors

GOOD NEWS
10.7.7.7.9.
Alternate tunes: 298–302, 568–570

Seek Ye First

572

The optional descant can be sung with any verse.

WORDS: Verse 1 para. Matthew 6:33 Karen Lafferty; verses 2, 3 para. Matthew 7:7, 4:4 anon.
MUSIC: Karen Lafferty

SEEK YE FIRST
Irregular

Words and Music © 1972 CCCM Music/Universal Music-Brentwood Benson Publ. (admin. CapitolCMGPublishing.com)

573 Shepherd, Show Me How to Go

"'Feed My Sheep'" by Mary Baker Eddy

1. Shep-herd, show me how to go O'er the hill - side steep,
2. Thou wilt bind the stub-born will, Wound the cal - lous breast,
3. So, when day grows dark and cold, Tear or tri - umph harms,

How to gath - er, how to sow,— How to feed Thy sheep;
Make self - right - eous - ness be still, Break earth's stu - pid rest.
Lead Thy lamb - kins to the fold, Take them in Thine arms;

I will lis - ten for Thy voice, Lest my foot - steps stray;
Stran-gers on a bar - ren shore, La - b'ring long and lone,
Feed the hun - gry, heal the heart, Till the morn - ing's beam;

WORDS: Mary Baker Eddy
MUSIC: Raymond David Burkhart

JOSEPHINE
7.5.7.5.D.
Alternate tunes: 304–309, 574–576

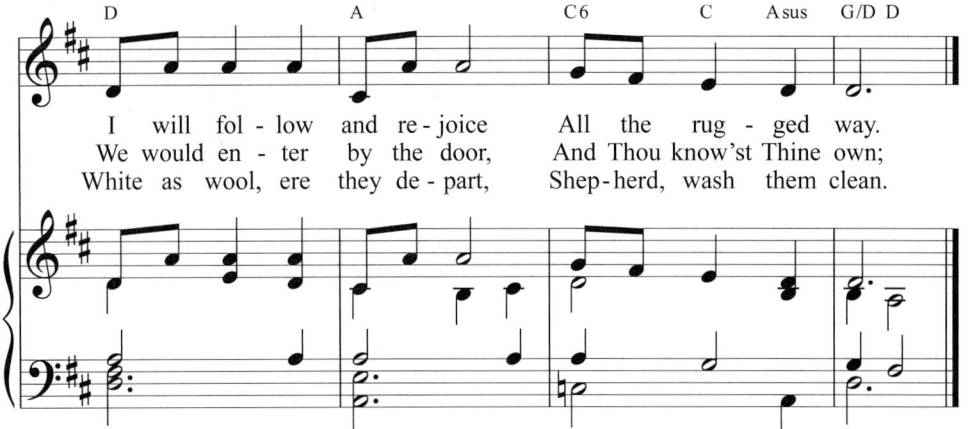

I will fol - low   and re - joice   All   the   rug - ged   way.
We would en - ter   by the door,   And Thou know'st Thine own;
White as wool, ere   they de - part,   Shep - herd, wash   them clean.

574 Shepherd, Show Me How to Go

"'Feed My Sheep'" by Mary Baker Eddy

1. Shep-herd, show me how to go O'er the hill-side steep, How to gath - er, how to sow,— How to feed Thy sheep; I will lis - ten

2. Thou wilt bind the stub-born will, Wound the cal - lous breast, Make self - right - eous - ness be still, Break earth's stu - pid rest. Stran-gers on a

3. So, when day grows dark and cold, Tear or tri-umph harms, Lead Thy lamb - kins to the fold, Take them in Thine arms; Feed the hun - gry,

WORDS: Mary Baker Eddy
MUSIC: Andrew D. Brewis, alt.

SASHA
7.5.7.5.D.
Alternate tunes: 304–309, 573, 575, 576

575 Shepherd, Show Me How to Go

"'Feed My Sheep'" by Mary Baker Eddy

1. Shep - herd, show me how to go O'er the hill - side steep,
2. Thou wilt bind the stub - born will, Wound the cal - lous breast,
3. So, when day grows dark and cold, Tear or tri - umph harms,

How to gath - er, how to sow,— How to feed Thy sheep;
Make self - right - eous - ness be still, Break earth's stu - pid rest.
Lead Thy lamb - kins to the fold, Take them in Thine arms;

I will lis - ten for Thy voice, Lest my foot - steps stray;
Stran - gers on a bar - ren shore, La - b'ring long and lone,
Feed the hun - gry, heal the heart, Till the morn - ing's beam;

I will fol - low and re - joice All the rug - ged way.
We would en - ter by the door, And Thou know'st Thine own;
White as wool, ere they de - part, Shep - herd, wash them clean.

WORDS: Mary Baker Eddy
MUSIC: Robert Rockabrand
Music © 2008 The Christian Science Board of Directors

HOW TO SOW
7.5.7.5.D.
Alternate tunes: 304–309, 573, 574, 576

Shepherd, Show Me How to Go   576

"'Feed My Sheep'" by Mary Baker Eddy

1. Shep-herd, show me how to go O'er the hill - side steep,
2. Thou wilt bind the stub-born will, Wound the cal - lous breast,
3. So, when day grows dark and cold, Tear or tri - umph harms,

How to gath - er, how to sow,— How to feed Thy sheep;
Make self-right - eous-ness be still, Break earth's stu - pid rest.
Lead Thy lamb - kins to the fold, Take them in Thine arms;

I will lis - ten for Thy voice, Lest my foot - steps stray;
Stran-gers on a bar-ren shore, La - b'ring long and lone,
Feed the hun - gry, heal the heart, Till the morn - ing's beam;

I will fol - low and re - joice All the rug - ged way.
We would en - ter by the door, And Thou know'st Thine own;
White as wool, ere they de - part, Shep-herd, wash them clean.

WORDS: Mary Baker Eddy
MUSIC: Swaziland melody; arr. CSPS

SIZOHAMBA
7.5.7.5.D.
Alternate tunes: 304–309, 573–575

Music arr. © 2016 The Christian Science Board of Directors

577 Sing a New, New Song

1. Sing a new, new song un-to the Lord,
And come in-to His courts with joy - ful voice;
Bless the Lord our God,

2. En-ter through His gates with thank-ful hearts,
And praise Him with the tim-brel, dance, and harp;
All the earth now sing,

3. Sing un-to the Lord, oh, all ye lands,
And make His praise re-sound from shore to shore;
Sing a new, new song,

Psalms 100:1, 2, 4; 148:3; 149:1.

WORDS: Para. Psalms Robert Rockabrand
MUSIC: Robert Rockabrand
SING AND PRAISE
9.10.5.7.8.Ref.

578

Sing a Song

1. Sing a song, sing a song to God, All the world
2. Great is God, wor - thy of all praise, Wor - ship God
3. Friends on earth, bow, con - fess God's might; Bow down and
4. Tell the na - tions God reigns su - preme, Judg - ing with

sing and bless God's name.
high a - bove all things. *Ay, ay, sa - li - dum -*
give all glo - ry due.
truth and right - eous - ness.

may,* ay, ay sa - li - dum - may.

Dai - ly sing of the
Spir - it's might made the
Come to God, bring your
Sing a song, sing a

*Pronounced *Sah-lee-doo-my*. This expression of gratitude, similar to "alleluia," comes from the Itneg people of the Philippines.

WORDS: Para. Psalm 96 Francisco F. Feliciano, alt.
MUSIC: Ben Pangosban; arr. CSPS

SALIDUMMAY
8.8.6.6.D.

sav - ing power, Tell all lands of the won - drous works.
u - ni - verse. Praise we give to God's maj - es - ty.
gifts most rare, Fill Love's hall with your joy - ful sound.
song to God, All the world sing and bless God's name.

Ay, ay, sa - li - dum - may, ay, ay sa - li - dum - may.

579

Take My Life

1. Take my life, and let it be Con‑se‑crat‑ed, Lord, to Thee.
2. Take my feet, and let them be Swift and beau‑ti‑ful for Thee.

Take my mo‑ments and my days, Let them flow in cease‑less praise.
Take my voice, and let me sing Al‑ways, on‑ly, for my King.

Take my hands, and let them move At the im‑pulse of Thy love.
Take my lips, and let them be Filled with mes‑sag‑es from

WORDS: Frances R. Havergal, adapt., alt.
MUSIC: Fenella Bennetts

Words adapt. © 1932, ren. 1960 The Christian Science Board of Directors
Music © 2006 Fenella Bennetts

CONSECRATION
7.7.7.7.7.7.
Alternate tune: 324, 580

580 Take My Life
Ten mi vida

WORDS: Frances R. Havergal, adapt.; Sp. tr. CSPS
MUSIC: William Dexheimer Pharris; arr. Mark Sedio, alt.

7.7.7.7.7.7.
Alternate tunes: 324, 579

There Are None Friendless

581

1. There are none friend - less, none a - fraid,
2. Truth sets us free from thought of sin;

The sav - ing Truth who know,
It heals all sor - row's blight.

Their shin - ing path leads from the shade,
Im - mor - tal joy is found there - in,

1 And up to light they go.
2 And there shall be no night.

3. And O, may we, God's chil - dren true,

God's heal - ing love make known,

And see by faith all things made new

When ruled by Love a - lone.

Proverbs 4:18 / II Corinthians 5:17 / Revelation 21:5; 22:5.

WORDS: William P. McKenzie, alt.
MUSIC: Jay Holcomb Frost
Music © 2017 The Christian Science Board of Directors

ANDALUCIA
C.M.
Alternate tune: 339

582 The Grace of God
A graça do Senhor

English
1. The grace of God is al - ways sur-round-ing me. Wher-
2. (For) - ev - er, Life di - vine, I am one with You. The
3. (The) strength of Love com-pels me to sing a - loud. In -

Portuguese
1. *A gra - ça do Se - nhor so - bre mim es - tá. Eu*
2. *(A) Vi - da e eu so - mos a - pe - nas um. O*
3. *(A) for - ça do A - mor me le - va a can - tar. A*

ev - er I should wan - der, God will ev - er be.
Christ re - veals my self-hood that is al - ways true.
tel - li - gent, e - ter - nal Mind will lift the cloud.

sin - to Sua pre - sen - ça a - on - de quer que eu vá.
Cris - to me re - ve - la o que sem - pre fui.
Men - te in - te - li - gen - te so - lu - ção me traz. A

WORDS: Leide Lessa; Eng. tr. CSPS
MUSIC: Messias R. Ullmann Fº

11.12.8.8.11.

583 The Lord Is My Light

1. The Lord is my light and my sal-va-tion. The Lord is my light and my sal-va-tion. The Lord is my light and my sal-va-tion. Whom shall I fear?

3. Wait on the Lord and be of good cour-age. Wait on the Lord and be of good cour-age. Whom shall I fear?

Refrain

Whom shall I fear? Whom shall I fear? The

Psalms 27:1, 5, 14.

WORDS: Lillian Bouknight
MUSIC: Lillian Bouknight; harm. CSPS

THE LORD IS MY LIGHT
Irregular

end here

Lord is the strength of my life. Whom shall I fear?

2. In the time of trou - ble He shall hide me.

In the time of trou - ble He shall hide me.

In the time of trou - ble He shall hide me.

return to beginning for verse 3 and Refrain

Whom shall I fear?

584 The Lord Is My Shepherd

1. The Lord is my Shep-herd; I need not a thing. Green
2. Love leads me in right paths to hon-or God's name, And
3. Though sin would sur-round me, my cup o-ver-flows; You

pas - tures give rest for my soul. Love
though I walk through dark-est days, I
show that I'm nev - er a - lone. Your

leads me be - side the still, still wa-ters. Love re-
won't be a - fraid for Love's here be - side me To pro-
good - ness and love are mine for - ev - er; In the

WORDS: Para. Psalm 23 Katie Grigg-Miller
MUSIC: Katie Grigg-Miller

SHEPHERD, LEAD ME HOME
Irregular

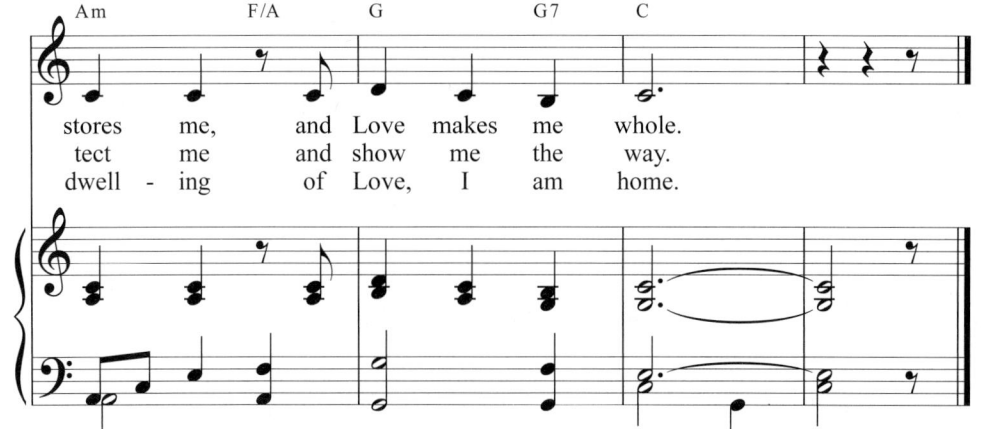

stores   me,   and Love makes me   whole.
tect   me   and show   me   the   way.
dwell - ing   of   Love, I   am   home.

585   This Is the Day

1. This is the day the Lord has made; Be glad, give thanks, re-joice; Stand in God's pres-ence, un-a-fraid, In praise lift up your voice. All
2. The Lord will hear be-fore we call, And ev-ery need sup-ply; Good things are free-ly given to all Who on God's word re-ly. We
3. For sin de-stroyed, for sor-row healed, For health and peace re-stored; For Life and Love by Truth re-vealed, We thank and bless the Lord. This

Psalms 118:24 / Isaiah 40:9 / James 1:17 / Revelation 7:9.

WORDS: Laura Lee Randall, alt.
MUSIC: Jonathan Roberts

SUNBEAM
C.M.D.
Alternate tune: 342

586   This Is the Day

Éste es el día

The music of this hymn is in the style of a *Chaya*. From the Diaguita culture of northern Argentina, a *Chaya* is a festive song, part of a harvest celebration involving singing, dancing, and games.

WORDS: Pablo Sosa, adapt.; Eng. tr. Mary Louise Bringle, adapt.
MUSIC: Pablo Sosa; harm. and arr. CSPS

ÉSTE ES EL DÍA
11.10.11.10.Ref.

Let us be glad as we pass through those gates.
Of - fering sal - va - tion with grace up - on grace.
I have seen mar - vel - ous, mar - vel - ous things.

en - tra - ré pa - ra a - la - bar al Se - ñor.
y por - que fuis - te mi gran sal - va - ción.
¡Qué ma - ra - vi - lla po - der ver - lo hoy!

There is the place where the right - eous may en - ter,
Turn - ing the stone that the build - ers re - ject - ed,
This is the day that the Lord has cre - at - ed;

És - ta es la puer - ta que Dios nos ha da - do,
És - ta es la pie - dra que fue de - se - cha - da.
És - te es el dí - a que el Se - ñor ha he - cho;

to Refrain

Sing - ing to God with thanks - giv - ing and praise.
In - to the cor - ner - stone, rock of our faith.
Join the re - joic - ing as ev - ery heart sings.

to - dos los jus - tos por e - lla en - tra - rán.
Ha vuel - to a - ho - ra a ser fun - da - men - tal.
con a - le - grí - a a - la - be - mos en Él.

587 There Is a Presence

1. There is a pres-ence walks with us On ev-ery path-less way,
2. A-bove the mist, a-bove the dark, A-bove the threats of fear,

A light out-shin-ing mid-day sun How-ev-er dark the day.
Up-held by Love that nev-er fails And is for-ev-er near.

We reach our hand—and feel God near; We cry—and She re-plies.
We can-not stray be-yond Love's care, For Love does fill all space;

We o-pen eyes that sense had dimmed; We stretch our wings and rise
And where we go the path is marked By an-gels of Love's grace.

The words of this hymn are from a poem entitled "Love's ever-presence," printed in the July 25, 1988 issue of the *Christian Science Sentinel*.

WORDS: Kathryn Paulson Grounds, alt.
MUSIC: Peter Johnson

CECILE
C.M.D.

Though I May Speak

1. Though I may speak with mov-ing words, Which can in-spire the hu-man heart, But have no love to seal their worth, They are but sham and emp-ty art.

2. Though I may give my world-ly goods, With-out a thought of self or gain, Un-less they bear the fruits of love, They are as clouds with-out their rain.

3. Though I may search the deep-est books, Com-pan-ion with the wis-est men, God's lov-ing voice still calls to me, It bids me turn and look a-gain.

4. Now I would learn to know this Love Through meek and pa-tient min-is-try, Un-til my life has grown a-new And Love is All - in - all to me.

I Corinthians 13. See hymn 497 for notes about this music.

WORDS: Fenella Bennetts, alt.
MUSIC: British melody; arr. Fenella Bennetts

O WALY WALY
L.M.
Alternate arr.: 497

589 Through Pure Love

1. Through pure love, God has command - ed
2. Je - sus' grace re - vealed God's good - ness,
3. God has made us in Love's im - age,
4. We are one with God for - ev - er,

Heal - ing light to shine on earth. And in our hearts there
Giv - ing hope to all the world. Love is the light that
Per - fect, Christ - like, pure, and free. We all re - flect this
One with Love e - ter - nal - ly— A per - fect bond that

beams the same love—Let the love of Christ shine bright.
burns with-in us— Let the life of Christ shine bright.
strength and pow - er— Let the mind of Christ shine bright.
can't be bro - ken—Let the truth of Christ shine bright.

Isaiah 60:1 / I Corinthians 2:16 / Ephesians 5:14. Although the music speaks clearly even when the rhythms are performed precisely as notated, a steady, triplet-based, swing rhythm, communicating a subtle sense of lightness, is appropriate for this style.

WORDS: Janet Hegarty
MUSIC: James H. Hegarty

RISE AND SHINE
8.7.9.7.Ref.

590   To God Compose a Song of Joy

1. To God com - pose a song of joy; To God make
2. Be - fore the na - tions God re - veals A just and
3. In ev - ery cor - ner of the earth, God comes to
4. Let seas in all their full - ness roar; Sing, peo - ple
5. The God of jus - tice comes to save; Let earth make

mel - o - dy, Whose arm of strength does won - drous
right - eous will, With stead - fast love and faith - ful -
save and free; Break forth with shouts of ho - ly
of all lands; Let moun - tains join and shout for
mel - o - dy; For God will judge with right - eous -

things, Whose hand brings vic - to - ry!
ness God loves all peo - ple still.
joy; All lands, make mel - o - dy.
joy; Let riv - ers clap their hands.
ness And rule with eq - ui - ty.

Psalms 86:10; 98:1–9 / Ephesians 5:19.

WORDS: Ruth Duck, alt.
MUSIC: Edwin R. Taylor

KEDDY
C.M.

We Cannot Turn Away from God 591

1. We can-not turn a - way from God   Be-cause, which - ev - er
2. Wheth - er we turn to left or right,   To north or south or
3. Wheth - er we plunge to o - cean trench   Or plot our course for
4. Wheth - er we build for cen - turies hence   Or let to - mor - row

way we face, Spir - it is there.   In ev - ery place,
east or west, We meet with Love—   and we are blessed.
far - thest space, Love's law con - trols.   What - ev - er race We
bound our aim, God sets the pace.   Al - ways the same, With

Ev - ery di - rec - tion, ev - ery-where,   Spir - it is there.
Up - ward or down, be - low, a - bove,   We meet with Love.
en - ter toward what - ev - er goals,   Love's law con - trols.
in - stant and e - ter - nal grace,   God sets the pace.

Psalms 139:7–10 / Hebrews 12:1. The words of this hymn are from a poem called "All-Presence," printed in the November 18, 1972 issue of the *Christian Science Sentinel*.

WORDS: Peter J. Henniker-Heaton
MUSIC: Kevin McCarter

CHAPEL HILL
8.8.4.4.8.4.

592 We Are Walking in the Light of God

Refrain

1. We are walk - ing in the light of God, We are
2. We are pray - ing in the light of God, We are
3. We are sing - ing in the light of God, We are

Zulu *Si - ya - hamb' e - ku - kha - nyen' kwen - khos', Si - ya -*

walk-ing in the light of God. We are walk - ing in the
pray-ing in the light of God. We are pray - ing in the
sing-ing in the light of God. We are sing - ing in the

hamb' e - ku - kha-nyen' kwen - khos', Si - ya - hamb' e - ku - kha -

light of God, We are walk - ing in the light of God.
light of God, We are pray - ing in the light of God.
light of God, We are sing - ing in the light of God.

nyen' kwen - khos', Si - ya - hamb' e - ku - kha-nyen' kwen - khos',

We are walk-ing, we are walk-ing, ooh We are
We are pray-ing, we are pray-ing, ooh We are
We are walk-ing, we are pray-ing, ooh We are

Si - ya - ham - ba, Si - ya - ham - ba, ooh Si - ya -

walk-ing in the light of God. We are walk-ing, we are
pray-ing in the light of God. We are pray-ing, we are
sing-ing in the light of God. We are walk-ing, we are

hamb' e - ku - kha-nyen' kwen - khos'. Si - ya - ham - ba, Si - ya -

*Pronounced: See-yah-hahm-bah-ku-kah-nyen-kwen-kos

The refrain of this hymn comes from a well-known South African freedom song. New words, echoing the sense of
unity and joy, have been added to create a large-scale refrain-verse-refrain-verse-refrain structure.

WORDS: Refrain Zulu; Eng. tr. Gracia Grindal; verses Désirée Goyette, alt.
MUSIC: Refrain South African melody); arr. *Freedom Is Coming*, 1984, keyboard arr. Ed Bogas;
verse music Désirée Goyette, arr. Ed Bogas

SIYAHAMBA
12.12.12.13.Ref.

walk-ing, ooh   We are walk-ing in the light of God.
pray-ing, ooh   We are pray-ing in the light of God.
pray-ing, ooh   We are sing-ing in the light of God.

ham - ba, ooh   Si - ya - hamb' e - ku - kha-nyen' kwen - khos'.

Verses

1. We are all   God's chil - dren,   ex - pres-sions of   one Mind,
2. As we turn   our fac - es,   up to the light   of Life,

Liv-ing in   the ra - diance   of Spir-it all   di - vine.
Har-mo-ny   re - plac - es   all pain and fear and strife.

Ev-ery heart   and na - tion   is an-swer-ing   the call
See the heaven - ly har - vest   so boun-ti-ful - ly   poured,

to Refrain

To a true   sal - va - tion   know-ing God is All - in - all.
As we raise   our voic - es   be - ing all of one   ac - cord!

593 We Gather Together

1. We gather together to ask the Lord's blessing,
To sing of God's goodness as year turns to year.
We gather professing Your grace and Your blessing,

2. Your Spirit consoles us. We're safe in Your keeping.
When roads are uncharted, Your love shows the way.
Where new hope is springing You fill us with singing;

3. What, then, can we give You in praise for our journey,
When all the earth's treasures were Yours from the start?
We offer our labor, our love for our neighbors,

This music is based upon an old European melody, first published in 1626. It gained international exposure in 1877, when it was arranged by the influential Viennese chorus master Eduard Kremser (from whom the tune derives its name).

WORDS: Ruth Duck, original first line "In Joyful Thanksgiving," alt.
MUSIC: Valerius's *Nederlandtsch Gedenck-clanck*, 1626; harm. Eduard Kremser, alt.
Words © 2015 Hope Publishing Company

KREMSER
12.11.12.11.
Alternate arr.: 292

With thanks for the gos - pel that gath - ers us here.
Your pres - ence de - lights us with each dawn - ing day.
Our gifts and the wor - ship of each hand and heart.

594 We're Steadfastly Protected by Your Power

Von guten Mächten treu und still umgeben

English
1. We're stead - fast - ly pro - tec - ted by Your pow - er,
2. Your pure and qui - et love spreads o'er us deep - ly;

German
1. Von gu - ten Mäch - ten treu und still um - ge - ben,
2. Wenn sich die Stil - le nun tief um uns brei - tet,

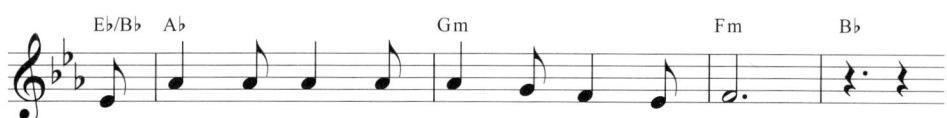

En - cir - cled in the car - ing arms of Love.
We know Your full - ness now and feel Your peace.

be - hü - tet und ge - trö - stet wun - der - bar,
so lass uns hö - ren je - nen vol - len Klang

To - geth - er, we are shar - ing all our days now,
For Your one ho - ly world of grace and pow - er,

so will Ich die - se Ta - ge mit euch le - ben
der Welt, die un - sicht - bar sich um uns wei - tet,

And year by year come bless - ings from a - bove.
We all praise You with joy that will not cease.

und mit euch ge - hen in ein neu - es Jahr.
all Dei - ner Kin - der ho - hen Lob - ge - sang.

The words of this hymn are based on a poem by Dietrich Bonhoeffer, written in prison. One of the most important German theologians of the 20th century, he was executed in 1945 as a result of his courageous resistance to Nazi fascism. His book *The Cost of Discipleship* is still widely read today.

WORDS: Dietrich Bonhoeffer; Eng. tr. and adapt. CSPS
MUSIC: Otto Abel; arr. CSPS

11.10.11.10.Ref.

Eng. tr. © 2017 The Christian Science Board of Directors
Music © Verlag Merseburger

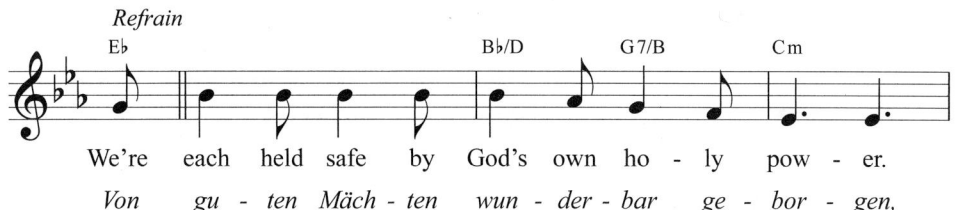

Refrain

We're each held safe by God's own ho - ly pow - er.
Von gu - ten Mäch - ten wun - der - bar ge - bor - gen,

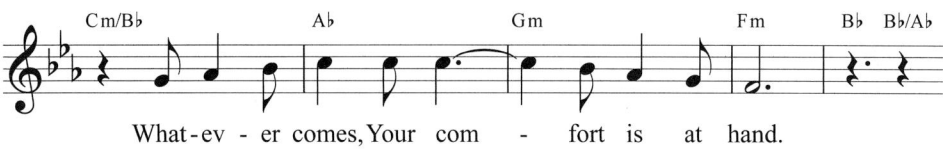

What-ev - er comes, Your com - fort is at hand.
er - war - ten wir ge - trost, was kom-men mag.

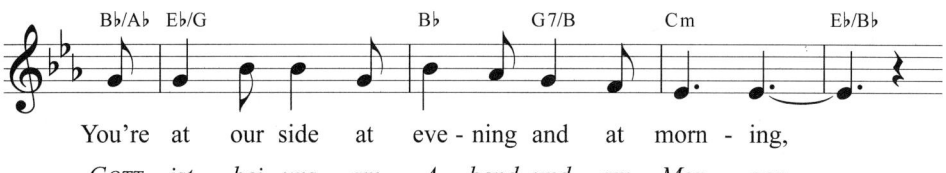

You're at our side at eve - ning and at morn - ing,
GOTT ist bei uns am A - bend und am Mor - gen

And each new day un - folds as You have planned.
und ganz ge - wiss an je - dem neu - en Tag.

595 When My Heart Is Lost in Sorrow

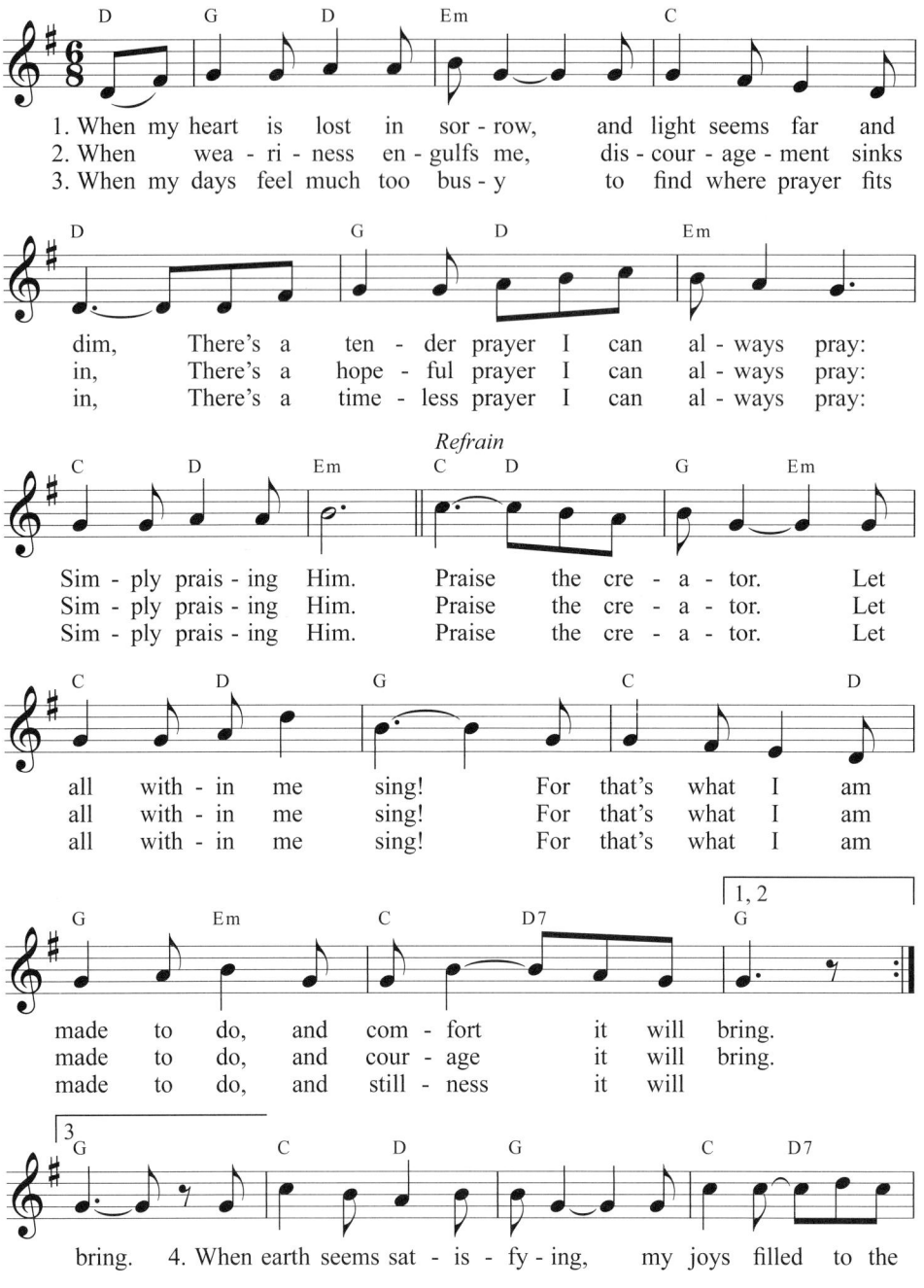

1. When my heart is lost in sor-row, and light seems far and
2. When wea-ri-ness en-gulfs me, dis-cour-age-ment sinks
3. When my days feel much too bus-y to find where prayer fits

dim, There's a ten-der prayer I can al-ways pray:
in, There's a hope-ful prayer I can al-ways pray:
in, There's a time-less prayer I can al-ways pray:

Refrain

Sim-ply prais-ing Him. Praise the cre-a-tor. Let
Sim-ply prais-ing Him. Praise the cre-a-tor. Let
Sim-ply prais-ing Him. Praise the cre-a-tor. Let

all with-in me sing! For that's what I am
all with-in me sing! For that's what I am
all with-in me sing! For that's what I am

1, 2

made to do, and com-fort it will bring.
made to do, and cour-age it will bring.
made to do, and still-ness it will

3

bring. 4. When earth seems sat-is-fy-ing, my joys filled to the

Psalms 96:1; 103:1.

WORDS: Susan Booth Mack Snipes, alt.
MUSIC: Susan Booth Mack Snipes; arr. Sue Loomis and Robert Rockabrand

SANCHEZ
Irregular

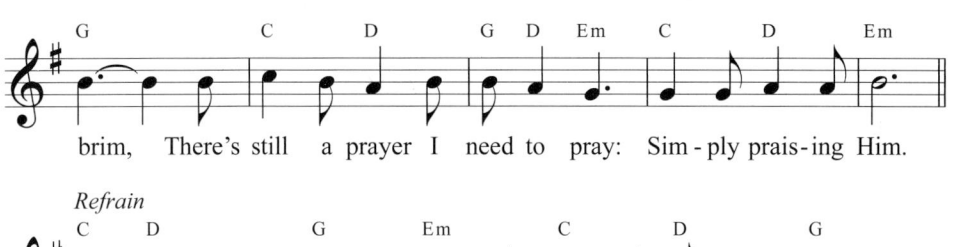

brim, There's still a prayer I need to pray: Sim-ply prais-ing Him.

Refrain

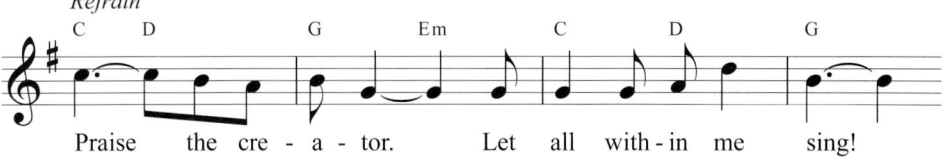

Praise the cre - a - tor. Let all with-in me sing!

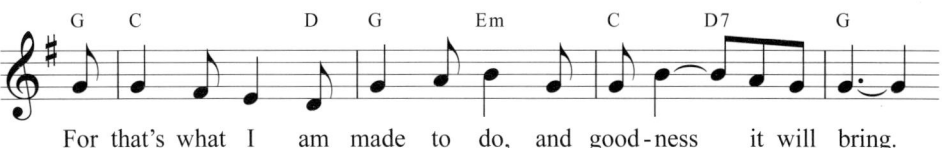

For that's what I am made to do, and good-ness it will bring.

For that's what we are made to do, let all the earth now sing!

When Peace, Like a River

1. When peace, like a riv - er, flows calm - ly each day, Or sor - rows like
2. Though ter - ror may buf - fet, my joy is in - nate. This un - chang - ing
3. Lord, has - ten the day when my faith shall be sight, The clouds be rolled

seas surge and roll, What - ev - er my lot, Love has taught me to
thought is my goal: That God has cre - at - ed my spir - i - tual
back as a scroll. When trum - pets shall sound and we all see the

Refrain

say, It is well, it is well with my soul. It is well (It is
state, And has giv - en me strength in my soul.
light, I will sing, it is well with my soul.

well) with my soul, (with my soul,) It is well, it is well with my soul.

II Kings 4:26 / Isaiah 34:4; 66:12 / Mark 10:52 / I Corinthians 15:52 / Revelation 6:14. This revival hymn, with a moving text by Horatio G. Spafford, was first published in the 1876 collection *Gospel Hymns No. 2*, the follow-up volume to *Gospel Hymns and Sacred Songs* (1875), compiled by Philip P. Bliss and Ira D. Sankey.

WORDS: Horatio G. Spafford, adapt.
MUSIC: Philip P. Bliss
Words adapt. © 2017 The Christian Science Board of Directors

VILLE DU HAVRE
11.8.11.9.Ref.

Where Charity and Love Abide   597

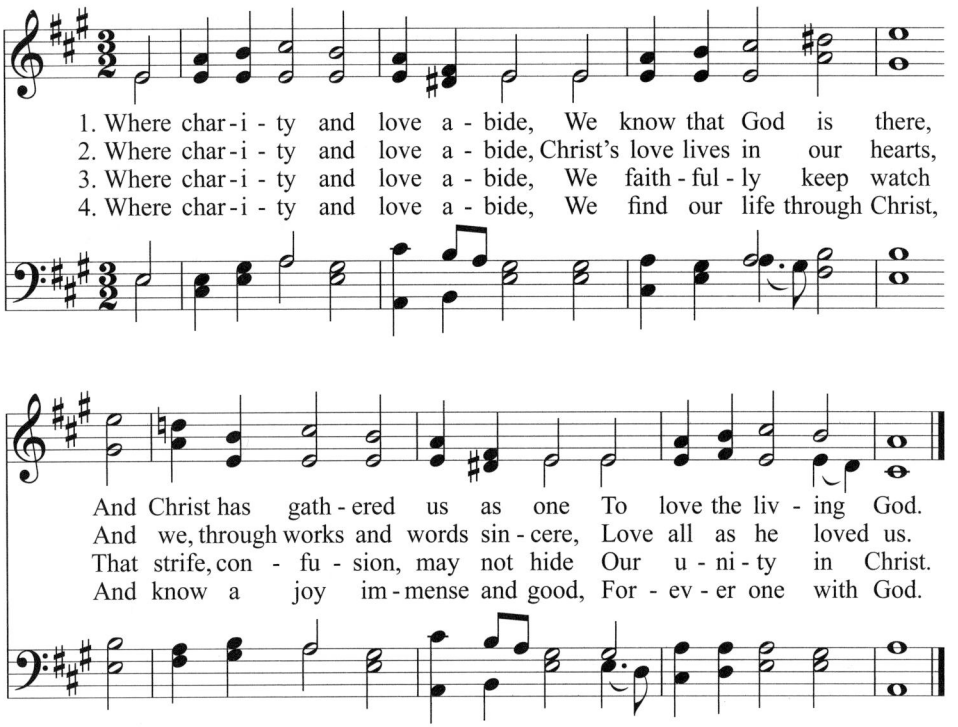

1. Where char-i-ty and love a-bide, We know that God is there,
2. Where char-i-ty and love a-bide, Christ's love lives in our hearts,
3. Where char-i-ty and love a-bide, We faith-ful-ly keep watch
4. Where char-i-ty and love a-bide, We find our life through Christ,

And Christ has gath-ered us as one To love the liv-ing God.
And we, through works and words sin-cere, Love all as he loved us.
That strife, con-fu-sion, may not hide Our u-ni-ty in Christ.
And know a joy im-mense and good, For-ev-er one with God.

John 13:34; 15:12 / I Corinthians 13:13. This hymn combines an adaptation of an early Christian poem from the Latin liturgy for Maundy Thursday with a 19th-century American hymn tune.

WORDS: Para. "Ubi Caritas" (9th c. Latin hymn) Kevin McCarter
MUSIC: Lucius Chapin

TWENTY-FOURTH
C.M.

Where You're Going, Love Will Lead You

598

1. Where you're go-ing, Love will lead you. Where you're walk-ing, Love will guide.
2. Let not want or lack con-fine you, Love is ev-er your sup-ply.

If you're hun-gry, Love will feed you. Love is al-ways at your side.
God's great good shall now de-fine you, As on Love your hopes re-ly.

When you're sleep-ing, Love will guard you. When you wak-en, com-fort give.
Though temp-ta-tion may as-sail you, Love will save you lest you stray.

Al-ways faith-ful, Love sur-rounds you, For by Love a-lone we live.
Love's pro-tec-tion nev-er fails you—God is Love and guards your way.

This text, joined here with a tune printed in several early 19th-century American shape-note hymnals, is from a poem entitled "Protection," first published in the October 10, 1925 issue of the *Christian Science Sentinel*.

WORDS: Elenora E. Pike, adapt.
MUSIC: American melody, Moore's *Columbian Harmony*, 1825; harm. CSPS
Words adapt. and Music harm. © 2016 The Christian Science Board of Directors

HOLY MANNA
8.7.8.7.D.

599 Whither Shall I Go from Thy Spirit

Descant

Grace un-to you and peace from a-bove.

Whith-er shall I go from Thy spir-

Peace from on high, from my

it? Or whith-er shall I flee from Thy

Spir - it. Be still and know I am

pres - ence? If I as-cend up in-to heav-en, Thou art

God. Be still and know that I am

there. If I make my bed in hell, Thou art

The music arrangement given here is based upon the version sung, a cappella, at the Adventure Unlimited (A/U) Ranches; a simple accompaniment and guitar chords have been added. The hymn may be sung twice, with the descant included the second time through.

WORDS: Psalms 139:7–10; desc. Psalms 46:10 and scriptural para.   WHITHER
MUSIC: Mark Shepherd; desc. anon.; transc. and arr. CSPS   Irregular

Music © 2008 The Christian Science Board of Directors
Music arr. © 2016 The Christian Science Board of Directors

600   Who Was That Man in Galilee

1. Who was that man in Gal - i - lee,
2. Why are we here, and who are we?
3. Christ is the light with which we shine,

Heal-ing and teach-ing be-side the sea? What was the power that
What is his pur - pose for you and me? Our lit - tle light seems
Lit from with-in by this love di - vine. Step out with cour - age,

made him strong? How can we learn to sing his song?
small and dim Next to the blaze that comes from him!
dare to go, Give from the heart the love you know.

Matthew 5:13–16 / John 8:12.

WORDS: Fenella Bennetts and Robert Witney
MUSIC: Andrew D. Brewis

LIGHT
8.9.8.8.Ref.

601 With One Accord in One Place

1. With one ac-cord in one place, In joy-ful praise of God's grace, We
2. Of one ac-cord, of one Mind, Our heal-ing mis-sion we find. We

join to-geth-er in one di-vine em - brace. A
pray to-geth-er—our lives in wor - ship bind. The

rush-ing might-y Spir - it De-scends from heav - en, hear it:
Com-fort-er is with us; Its pres-ence here as-sures us:

Acts 2:1, 2.

WORDS: James R. Corbett
MUSIC: Ryan Vigil

ONE ACCORD
7.7.11.7.7.5.5.6.5.5.6.

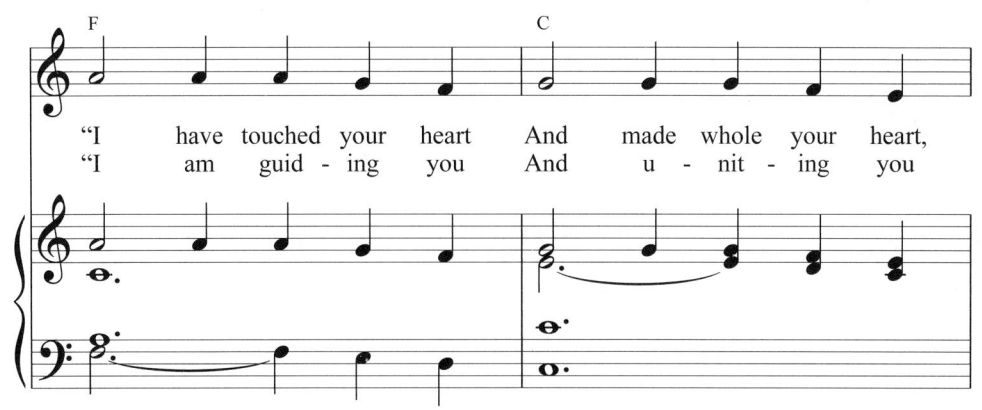

"I have touched your heart And made whole your heart,
"I am guid - ing you And u - nit - ing you

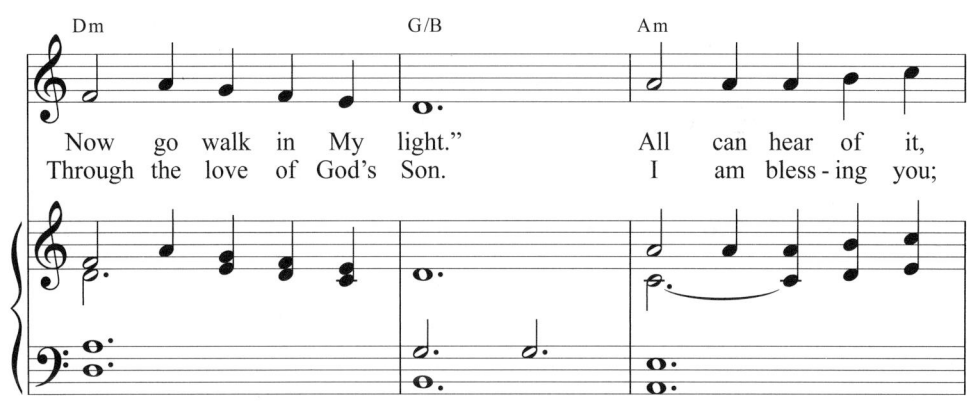

Now go walk in My light." All can hear of it,
Through the love of God's Son. I am bless - ing you;

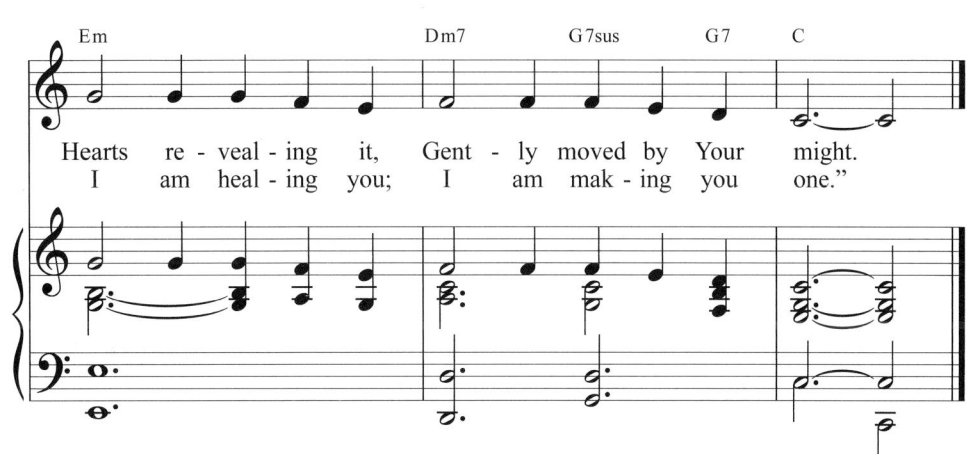

Hearts re - veal - ing it, Gent - ly moved by Your might.
I am heal - ing you; I am mak - ing you one."

602 You Know My Words

1. You know my words be-fore they're said. You know my
3. Our ev-ery thought, each word we say, The whole of

need and I am fed. You give me life. You
time, the pres-ent day, Are held with-in Your

know my ways, My strength, my path, for all my days.
might-y hand, Too won-der-ful to com-pre-hend!

2. If I should fly be-yond the dawn, The dark-ness
4. O mend my heart and free my voice, From sin re-

Psalms 139:1, 3, 6, 9, 11, 23.

WORDS: Laurie Zelman
MUSIC: Scottish melody; arr. John L. Bell, alt.

YE BANKS AND BRAES
L.M.D.
Alternate tune: 603

will   not   o - ver - come. If   I   lie   down   in
leased,   I   will   re - joice. O   search   me,   Lord,   my

deep - est night, Still You   are   there, my   Lord,   my   light.
spir - it   cries,   And   let   my   song   of   praise   a - rise!

603
You Know My Words

1. You know my words be-fore they're said. You
2. If I should fly be-yond the dawn, The
3. Our ev-ery thought, each word we say, The

know my need and I am fed. You give me life. You
dark-ness will not o-ver-come. If I lie down in
whole of time, the pres-ent day, Are held with-in Your

know my ways, My strength, my path, for all my days, My
deep-est night, Still You are there, my Lord, my light, Still
might-y hand, Too won-der-ful to com-pre-hend, Too

strength, my path, for all my days.
You are there, my Lord, my light.
won-der-ful to com-pre-hend! 4. O

Psalms 139:1, 3, 6, 9, 11, 23.

WORDS: Laurie Zelman
MUSIC: Mark A. Miller; arr. CSPS
Words and Music © 2003 Abingdon Press (admin. Music Services)

HIXON
L.M.
Alternate tune: 602

FULL-SCORE APPENDIX

(fs) 432 Above All Earthly Gain

Plutôt que tous les gains

English
1. A - bove all earth - ly gain,   I
2. When, in hu - mil - i - ty,   I
3. Dear Love, rule out the fears   From

French
1. Plu - tôt que tous les gains,   J'as -
2. Ou - vrant mon cœur, je peux   Res -
3. E - li - mi - ne les peurs   De

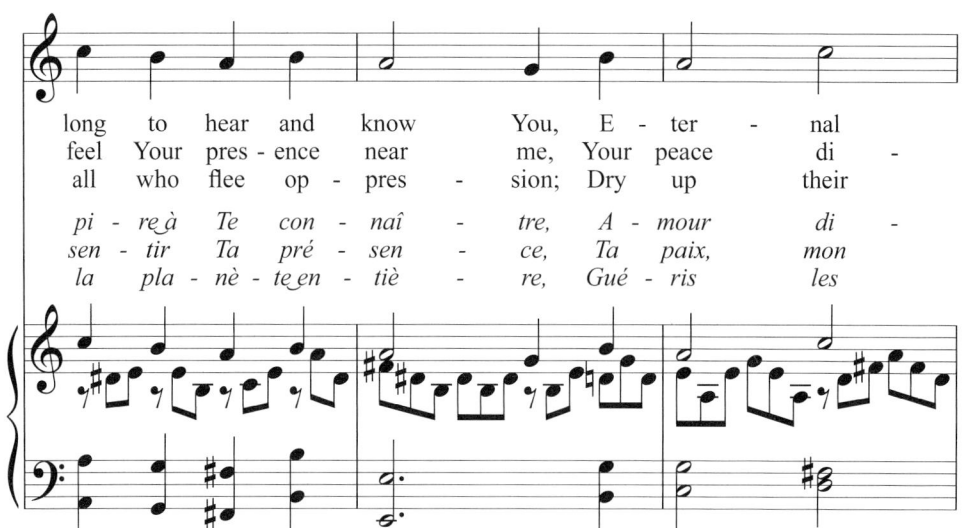

long to hear and know You, E - ter - nal
feel Your pres - ence near me, Your peace di -
all who flee op - pres - sion; Dry up their

pi - re_à Te con - naî - tre, A - mour di -
sen - tir Ta pré - sen - ce, Ta paix, mon
la pla - nè - te_en - tiè - re, Gué - ris les

These words are from a poem, entitled "Migration," written specifically to fit this melody. The music is adapted from Gabriel Fauré's *Cantique de Jean Racine*, a work that earned the composer first prize as a student at the Ecole Niedermeyer in 1865.

WORDS: Josette Flamand, incl. Eng. tr.
MUSIC: Gabriel Fauré; adapt. and arr. CSPS

Irregular

Fr. Words, Eng. tr., Music arr. © 2016 The Christian Science Board of Directors

har - mo - ny; Your good - ness is re -
l'har - mo - nie, Et Ta bon - té par -

vealed And here for all to see.
fai - te A tout ja - mais s'ac - com - plit.

Brood O'er Us

Oh, bajo Tu ala tutelar

"Love" by Mary Baker Eddy

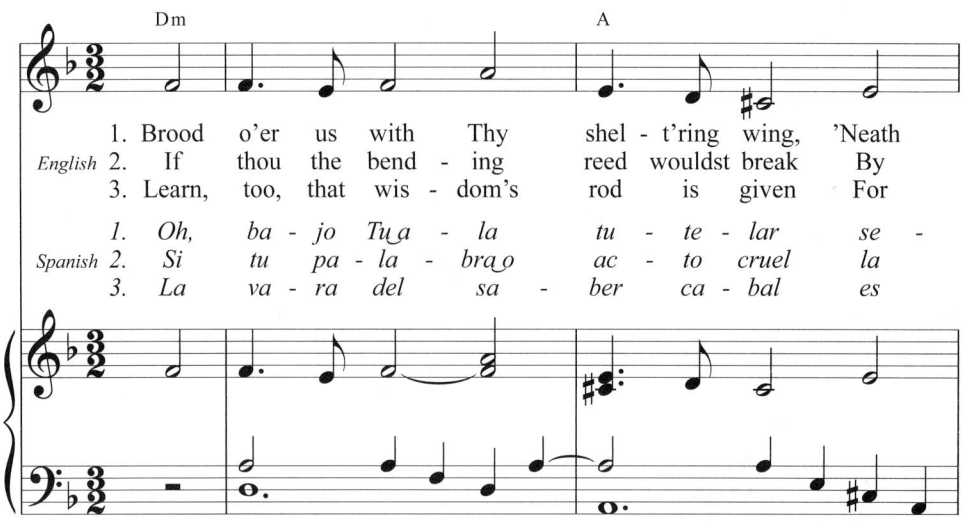

English
1. Brood o'er us with Thy shel-t'ring wing, 'Neath
2. If thou the bend-ing reed wouldst break By
3. Learn, too, that wis-dom's rod is given For

Spanish
1. Oh, ba-jo Tu a-la tu-te-lar se-
2. Si tu pa-la-bra_o ac-to cruel la
3. La va-ra del sa-ber ca-bal es

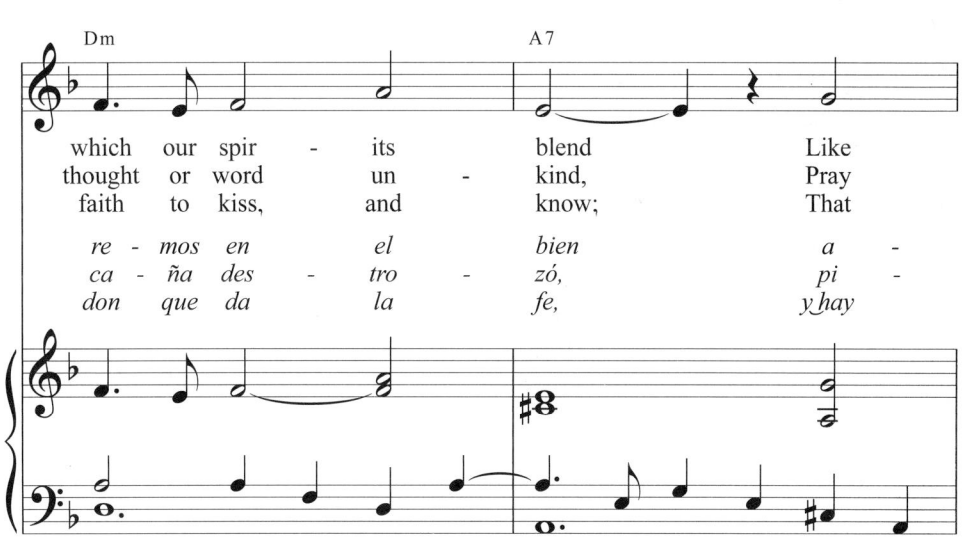

which our spir-its blend Like
thought or word un-kind, Pray
faith to kiss, and know; That

re-mos en el bien a-
ca-ña des-tro-zó, pi-
don que da la fe, y_hay

WORDS: Mary Baker Eddy; Sp. tr. CSPS
MUSIC: Melanie H. Alcázar; arr. CSPS

LOVE
8.6.8.6.8.8.
Alternate tunes: 30–32, 452–454, 456

Sp. tr. © 1946, ren. 1974 The Christian Science Board of Directors
Music © 2016 The Christian Science Board of Directors

not | from those who watch | and love.
make | men one in love | re - main.
chas - | tens pride and earth - | born fear,

par - te del de - vo - to a - mor.
to - dos u - ne en el a - mor.
mi - lla or - gu - llo y te - mor.

English	Spanish
4. Through God, who gave that word of might Which swelled creation's lay: "Let there be light, and there was light." What chased the clouds away? 'Twas Love whose finger traced aloud A bow of promise on the cloud.	4. *Dios hizo con Su voz nacer* *de Sí la creación:* *"Sea la luz; y fue la luz."* *¿Quién nubes disipó?* *Amor, que traza la feraz* *promesa en iris fiel de paz.*
5. Thou to whose power our hope we give, Free us from human strife. Fed by Thy love divine we live, For Love alone is Life; And life most sweet, as heart to heart Speaks kindly when we meet and part.	5. *Tú, que esperanza a todos das,* *nos libras del rencor.* *Tu amor la vida es en verdad,* *pues Vida es sólo Amor;* *muy dulce vida si al hablar* *lo hacemos siempre con bondad.*

Brood O'er Us

"Love" by Mary Baker Eddy

1. Brood o'er us with Thy shel-t'ring wing, 'Neath which our spir-its blend Like broth-er birds, that soar and sing, And on the same branch bend. The ar-row that doth

WORDS: Mary Baker Eddy
MUSIC: Peter B. Allen
Music © 2008 The Christian Science Board of Directors

NOCTURNE
8.6.8.6.8.8.
Alternate tunes: 30–32, 452–455

wound the dove   Darts not from those who watch   and love.

2. If   thou   the   bend - ing   reed wouldst break   By
3. Learn, too,   that   wis - dom's   rod   is   given   For

thought or word un - kind,   Pray that   his spir - it   you par-
faith   to kiss, and know;   That greet-ings glo - rious from high

Come, Gracious Spirit

459 (fs)

1. Come, gra-cious Spir-it, heaven-ly Love,
2. The light of Truth to us dis-play,

With light and com-fort from a-bove;
That we may know and choose Your way;

Be Truth our guard-ian, Love our guide,
Plant ho-ly joy in ev-ery heart,

O'er
That

WORDS: Simon Browne, adapt., alt.
MUSIC: Andrew D. Brewis

ORCHARDS
L.M.
Alternate tune: 39

ev-ery thought and step pre-side,   Be God our guide.
we from You may ne'er de-

part,   Plant joy in ev-ery heart.

3. Lead us, O Christ, the liv - ing Way,

467 Eternal Mind the Potter Is

Matthew 6:10 / Luke 11:2 / Romans 8:17.

WORDS: Mary Alice Dayton
MUSIC: Andrew D. Brewis
Music © 2011 Andrew D. Brewis

FRIEND
C.M.D.
Alternate tunes: 51, 52, 468

God Created Us in His Own Image 482

Deus criou o homem de Si mesmo

English

1. God cre-at - ed us in His own im - age,
2. Ev - ery-thing our Mas-ter Je - sus taught us

Portuguese

1. Deus cri-ou o ho-mem de Si mes - mo,
2. Tu-do o que Je - sus nos en - si - nou,

All the u - ni - verse is His cre - a - tion too;
Showed the way to love each oth - er dear - ly,

To - do o u - ni - ver-so E - le cri - ou tam - bém.
Foi a - mar os nos-sos se - me - lhan - tes.

He cre - at - ed us as His re - flec - tion,
When he healed the sick and freed the sin - ner,

Fez o ho - mem se - me - lhan-te a E - le,
E por ver as - sim tão bem o ho - mem

WORDS: Graça de Maria Amorim dos Santos; Eng. tr. CSPS
MUSIC: Graça de Maria Amorim dos Santos; arr. CSPS

Irregular

Port. Words, Eng. tr., Music © 2017 The Christian Science Board of Directors

Knowing how to see reality, Pure and innocent and free,
We shall come to see reality, Pure and innocent and free,

Vemos a realidade, Pura, inocente,—
Vemos a realidade, Pura, inocente,—

Made in the likeness of our God.
Made in the likeness of our God.

A criação de Deus.
A criação de Deus.

Refrain

This clear view of man is perfect,

Essa percepção do homem,

fs 489 Halle, Halle, Hallelujah

Psalm 150. The refrain of this hymn comes from a traditional Caribbean song, to which composer-arranger
Hal Hopson has added new words and music for the verses. The hymn begins with the refrain, which leads directly
to verse 1; the refrain is then repeated, followed by verse 2; and the hymn ends with a final statement of the refrain.

WORDS: Para. Psalm 150 Hal H. Hopson
MUSIC: Refrain, Caribbean melody; arr. and additional music Hal H. Hopson
HALLE, HALLE
7.7.9.7.7.9.Ref.
Words and Music © 1998 Hope Publishing Company

end here

lu - jah, hal - le - lu - jah.

Verses

1. Praise God in this ho - ly place, Ev - ery na - tion, ev - ery race.
2. Ev - ery-thing that breathes now praise, Sing your songs, let voic - es raise.

Come, make joy - ful mu - sic to the Lord.
Come, make joy - ful mu - sic to the Lord.

Sound the trum-pet, sound it clear, Sound it for the world to hear.
Play the cym-bals, play the lute; Play the tim-brel, play the flute.

to Refrain

Come, make joy-ful mu-sic to the Lord.
Come, make joy-ful mu-sic to the Lord.

I Awake Each Morn

500 (fs)

1. I a - wake each morn to a brand - new day, Sing - ing
2. (I can) walk with Love through the val - ley of fear, Sing - ing

Hal - le - lu - jah! as I go on my way, For my
Hal - le - lu - jah! O, my Sav - ior is here! For my

heart is fixed on this one guar - an - tee: The
emp - ty long - ing no hope can ful - fill, But

Psalms 23:4.

WORDS and MUSIC: Susan Booth Mack Snipes
Words and Music © 2007 In Our Field Productions

DALTON
Irregular

I Love Your Way of Freedom, Lord 501 (fs)

1. I love Your way of free-dom, Lord, To serve You is my
2. Though storm or dis-cord cross my path Your power is still my

choice; In Your clear light of Truth I rise And,
stay, Though hu-man will and woe would check My

lis - ten-ing for Your voice, I hear Your prom-ise
up - ward - soar - ing way; All un - a - fraid I

Exodus 33:14 / I Corinthians 13:12.

WORDS: Violet Hay, alt.
MUSIC: Andrew D. Brewis
Words © 1931, ren. 1959 The Christian Science Board of Directors
Music © 2007 Andrew D. Brewis

FOCUS
C.M.D.
Alternate tune: 136

fs 513 It Matters Not What Be Thy Lot

"Satisfied" by Mary Baker Eddy

1. It mat-ters not what be thy lot, So
3. Aye, dark-ling sense, a-rise, go hence! Our

Love doth guide; For storm or shine,
God is good. False fears are foes—

pure peace is thine, What-e'er be - tide.
truth tat-ters those, When un - der - stood.

WORDS: Mary Baker Eddy
MUSIC: Andrew D. Brewis
Music © 2008 The Christian Science Board of Directors

MKHAYA
8.4.8.4.
Alternate tunes: 160–162, 514, 515

2. And of these stones, or ty-rants' thrones, God
4. Love loos-eth thee, and lift-eth me, A-

a - ble is To raise up seed— in
yont hate's thrall: There Life is light, and

thought and deed— To faith - ful His.
wis - dom might, And God is All.

It Matters Not What Be Thy Lot 514 (fs)

"Satisfied" by Mary Baker Eddy

1. It mat-ters not what be thy lot, So Love doth guide; For storm or shine, pure peace is thine, What-e'er be-tide. 2. And

WORDS: Mary Baker Eddy
MUSIC: Mindy Jostyn; arr. CSPS

HUDSON
8.4.8.4.
Alternate tunes 160–162, 513, 515

517 Joyfully We're Singing
Canto de alegría

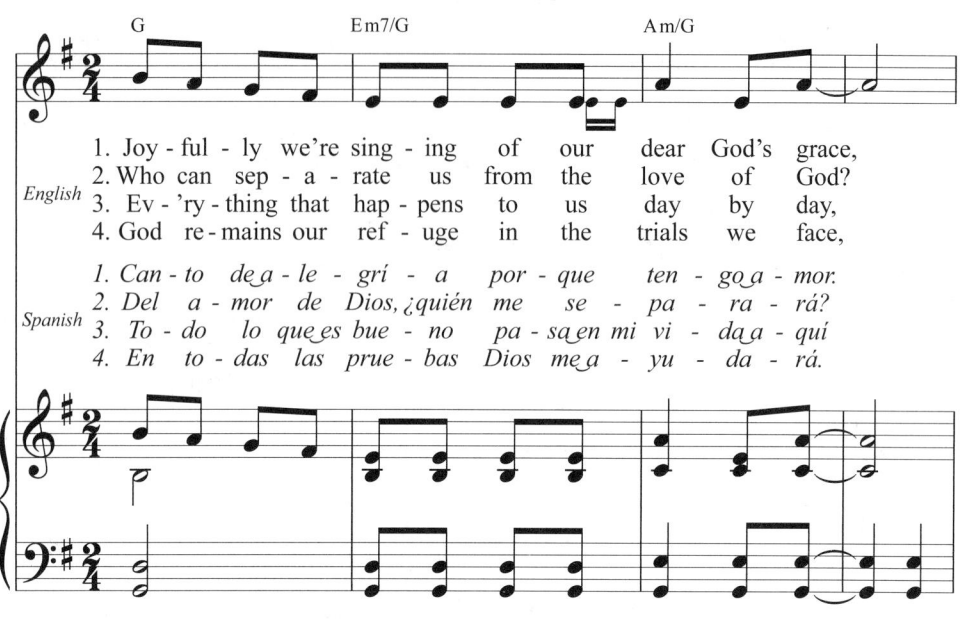

English
1. Joy-ful-ly we're sing-ing of our dear God's grace,
2. Who can sep-a-rate us from the love of God?
3. Ev-'ry-thing that hap-pens to us day by day,
4. God re-mains our ref-uge in the trials we face,

Spanish
1. Can-to de a-le-grí-a por-que ten-go a-mor.
2. Del a-mor de Dios, ¿quién me se-pa-ra-rá?
3. To-do lo que es bue-no pa-sa en mi vi-da a-quí
4. En to-das las prue-bas Dios me a-yu-da-rá.

Liv-ing ev-'ry day with-in Love's warm em-brace.
Truth is here to shield us with its staff and rod.
Christ will be the bea-con that will light our way.
Shield-ing and sus-tain-ing us with lov-ing grace.

Vi-vo ca-da dí-a con el Se-ñor.
Es-con-di-do en Dios, ¿quién me to-ca-rá?
Dios me lo pre-pa-ra y me pro-te-ge a-sí.
No me de-sam-pa-ra, no me de-ja-rá.

Romans 8:35, 37–39.

WORDS: Verses 1, 4 anon.; verses 2, 3 Enrique S. Turral; Eng. tr. Mary Louise Bringle, adapt.
MUSIC: Argentine melody; harm. Ronald Krisman, alt.
Eng. tr. and Music harm. © 2005 GIA Publications, Inc.

ARGENTINA
11.11.11.11.Ref.

G   **Em7/G**   **Am/G**

Ea - ger - ly we long to wit - ness ev - 'ry - where;
What is there to harm us when this help is sure?
Through dis - tress and per - il, God is faith - ful still,
Work - ing through the la - bors of our hearts and hands,

Quie - ro_a to - do_el mun - do de Él siem - pre_ha - blar.
Si Dios jus - ti - fi - ca, ¿quién con - de - na - rá?
En las prue - bas du - ras, Dios me_es siem - pre fiel:
Él me ne - ce - si - ta en Su o - bra ya.

D7   **C/G**   **G**

All through - out the world, God's sav - ing love to share.
We are more than con - quer - ors; we rest se - cure.
Why should we be fear - ful if we trust God's will?
Truth will lead us on - ward in tri - um - phant bands!

Quie - ro_a to - do_el mun - do Su a - mor do - nar.
Si Dios me de - fien - de, ¿quién me_a - cu - sa - rá?
¿por qué te - ner du - das, si des - can - so_en Él?
Se - gui - ré_a - de - lan - te, voy a tri - un - far,

Refrain
G   **Am**

Sing - ing of our dear God's grace,
Can - to por - que ten - go_a - mor.

Lean on the Sustaining Infinite 519 (fs)

1. Lean on the sus-tain-ing in - fi - nite And bless-ings will be yours. Lean not on per - son, place, or thing, Or e - co - nom - ic laws; But

2. Let the heal-ing reign of Truth and Life, The reign of Love di - vine, Be now es - tab-lished with - in me To show Soul's clear de - sign Of

3. Love with a heart of ten - der - ness Your en - e - mies and friends; How - ev - er hard this may ap - pear, This qual - i - ty just mends. For

The words of this hymn are from a poem entitled "Three I's for life," printed in the January 13, 2013 issue of the *Christian Science Sentinel.* The poem references the opening line of *Science and Health with Key to The Scriptures,* by Mary Baker Eddy: "To those leaning on the sustaining infinite, to-day is big with blessings."

WORDS: Jill Gooding, alt.
MUSIC: Andrew D. Brewis

SUSTAINING
Irregular

524 Like a River That Runs to the Ocean

Refrain

Like a riv-er that runs to the o-cean,
Like a ray reach-ing out from the sun,
Like a branch and the tree, a drop and the sea,
I and my Fa-ther are one.

end here

WORDS: Mindy Jostyn, alt.
MUSIC: Mindy Jostyn; arr. CSPS

ONE
Irregular

O'er Waiting Harpstrings

551 (fs)

"Christ My Refuge" by Mary Baker Eddy

1. O'er wait-ing harp-strings of the mind There sweeps a strain, Low,
(3.) His un-veiled, sweet mer-cies show Life's bur-dens light.   I

sad, and sweet, whose mea-sures bind The power of pain,   2. And
kiss the cross, and wake to know A world more bright.   4. And

wake a white-winged an-gel throng Of thoughts, il-lumed   By
o'er earth's trou-bled, an-gry sea I see Christ walk,   And

WORDS: Mary Baker Eddy
MUSIC: Cherie Brennan
Music © 2017 The Christian Science Board of Directors

HEART SONG
8.4.8.4.
Alternate tunes: 253–257, 550, 552

552 O'er Waiting Harpstrings

"Christ My Refuge" by Mary Baker Eddy

1. O'er wait-ing harp-strings of the mind There sweeps a strain,
3. Then His un-veiled, sweet mer-cies show Life's bur-dens light.
6. From tir-ed joy and grief a-far, And near-er Thee,—

Low, sad, and sweet, whose mea-sures bind The power of pain,
I kiss the cross, and wake to know A world more bright.
Fa-ther, where Thine own chil-dren are, I love to be.

2. And wake a white-winged an-gel throng Of thoughts, il-lumed By
4. And o'er earth's trou-bled, an-gry sea I see Christ walk, And
7. My prayer, some dai-ly good to do To Thine, for Thee; An

WORDS: Mary Baker Eddy
MUSIC: Peter B. Allen
Music © 2016 The Christian Science Board of Directors

HARPSTRINGS
8.4.8.4.
Alternate tunes: 253–257, 550, 551

to beginning

C/G   A7   D9   G7sus   G7

waves can shock, Oh, nev - er - more!

✛ *Coda*

C/G   A7   D9   G7   C   Fm   C/E   D   D♭   C

Love, where - to God lead - eth me.

Our Father Which Art in Heaven 559 ⓕⓢ

The Lord's Prayer

Our Fa - ther which art in heav - en, Hal - low - ed be Thy name. Thy king - dom come. Thy will be done in earth, as it is in heav - en.

WORDS: Matthew 6:9–13
MUSIC: Wendy Wylie Winegar; arr. Randall Woltz
Music © 2016 The Christian Science Board of Directors

ASPIRATION
Irregular
Alternate tune: 558

565 # Rise Up and Walk

F   F/E   F/D   F/C   B♭   B♭/A

1. Rise up and walk, take up your bed. With these few words the
2. Cleanse the lep - ers, heal the sick. Cast out de - mons.

Gm7   C   F   F/E   F/D   F/C

sick - ness fled. Stretch forth your hand. Re - ceive your sight.
Raise the dead. Truth is re - vealed in ev - ery place,

B♭   B♭/A   Gm7   C   Gm   C7   Dm7

Je - sus' com-mands re - veal God's might. You are God's pur-pose,
Through-out all time, through-out all space. Right in this mo-ment,

Isaiah 44:23; 55:12 / Matthew 10:8; 12:13 / Mark 3:5 / Luke 5:23, 24; 18:42 / John 5:8; 14:12. The second verse of
this hymn quotes the words—drawn from the American Standard translation of the Bible—encircling the Cross and
Crown trademark that identifies the authorized writings of Mary Baker Eddy.

WORDS and MUSIC: Peter B. Allen
Words and Music © 2008 Peter B. Allen

RISE UP
Irregular

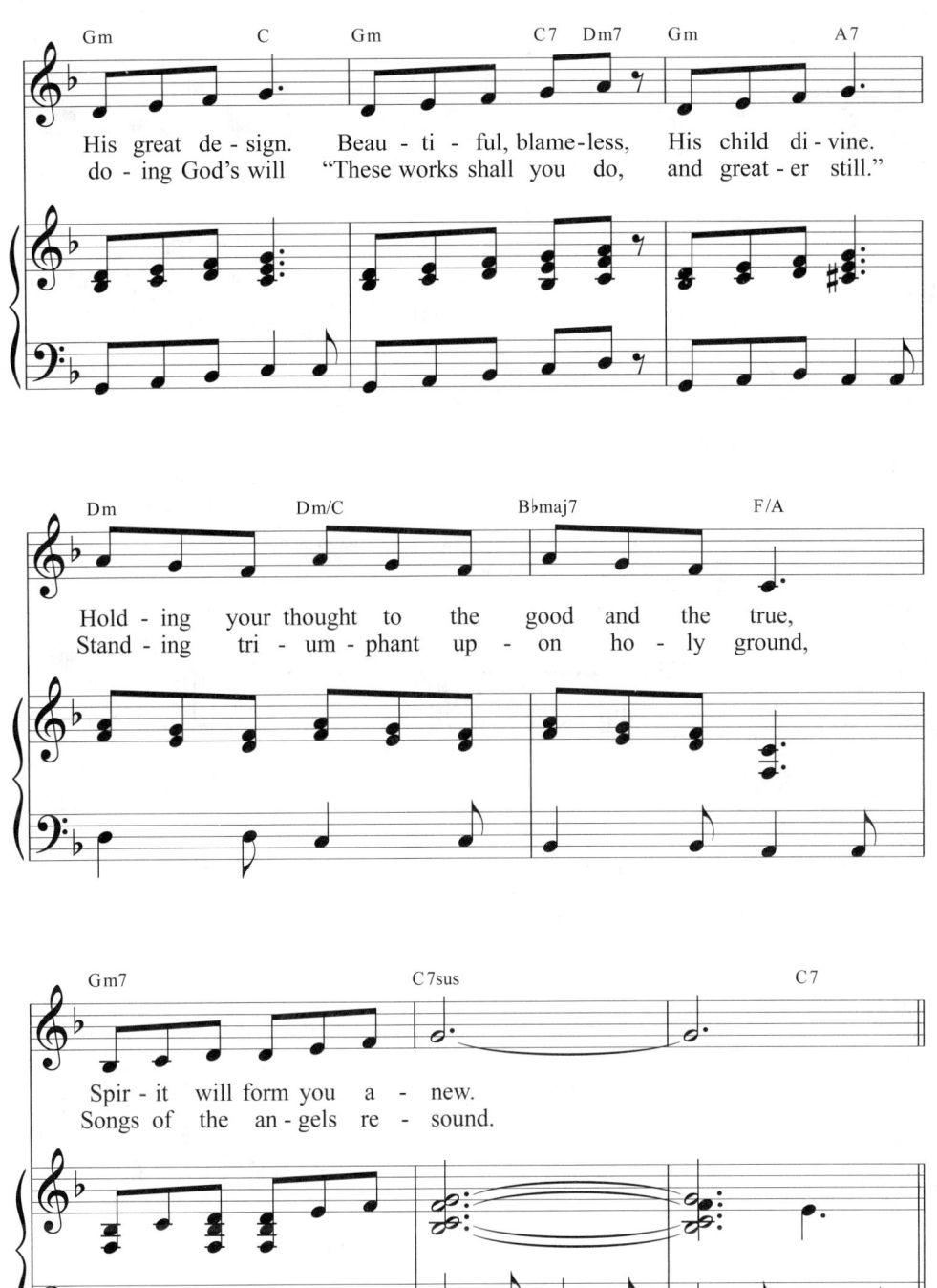

His great de-sign. Beau-ti-ful, blame-less, His child di-vine.
do-ing God's will "These works shall you do, and great-er still."

Hold-ing your thought to the good and the true,
Stand-ing tri-um-phant up-on ho-ly ground,

Spir-it will form you a-new.
Songs of the an-gels re-sound.

569 Saw Ye My Saviour?

"Communion Hymn" by Mary Baker Eddy

1. Saw ye my Sav - iour? Heard ye the glad sound?
2. Mourn - er, it calls you,— "Come to my bos - om,
4. Strong - est de - liv - erer, friend of the friend - less,

Felt ye the pow - er of the Word? 'Twas the
Love wipes your tears all a - way, And will
Life of all be - ing di - vine: Thou the

Truth that made us free, And was found by you and
lift the shade of gloom, And for you make ra - diant
Christ, and not the creed; Thou the Truth in thought and

WORDS: Mary Baker Eddy
MUSIC: Désirée Goyette
Music © 2008 The Christian Science Board of Directors

LINCOLN
10.7.7.7.9.
Alternate tunes: 298–302, 568, 570, 571

Spir-it that makes pure, That ex-alts thee, and will cure All thy

sor - row and sick - ness and sin."

to verse 4

Saw Ye My Saviour?

"Communion Hymn" by Mary Baker Eddy

571 (fs)

1. Saw ye my Saviour? Heard ye the glad sound? Felt ye the power of the Word? 'Twas the Truth that made us free, And was found by you and me In the
2. Mourner, it calls you,— "Come to my bosom, Love wipes your tears all away, And will lift the shade of gloom, And for you make radiant room Midst the
3. Sinner, it calls you,— "Come to this fountain, Cleanse the foul senses within; 'Tis the Spirit that makes pure, That exalts thee, and will cure All thy

WORDS: Mary Baker Eddy
MUSIC: Fenella Bennetts
Music © 2016 The Christian Science Board of Directors

GOOD NEWS
10.7.7.7.9.
Alternate tunes: 298–302, 568–570

life   and the love of our Lord.
glo - ries of one end-less day."
sor - row and sick-ness and   sin."

4. Strong - est de - liv - erer, friend of the friend - less,

Life   of all be - ing di - vine: Thou the

Christ, and not the creed; Thou the Truth in thought and deed; Thou the

wa - ter, the bread, and the wine.

Take My Life

Ten mi vida

English
1. Take my life, and let it be
3. Take my voice, and let me sing
5. Take my life, and let it be

Spanish
1. Ten mi vida, que estará
3. Ten mi voz, que cantará
5. Ten mi vida, que estará

Con - se - crat - ed, Lord, to Thee. Take my mo - ments and
Al - ways, on - ly, for my King. Take my lips, and let
Con - se - crat - ed, Lord, to Thee. I am Thine, and I

con - sa - gra - da a Ti, Se - ñor; ten mis dí - as, que
siem - pre y só - lo a Ti, Se - ñor; ten mis la - bios, que
con - sa - gra - da a Ti, Se - ñor; Tu - yo soy, y siem-

WORDS: Frances R. Havergal, adapt.; Sp. tr. CSPS
MUSIC: William Dexheimer Pharris; arr. Mark Sedio, alt.

7.7.7.7.7.7.
Alternate tunes: 324, 579

them be   Swift and beau - ti - ful   for Thee.
I   pour   At Thy feet   its   trea - sure store.

-   *ta - rán   siem - pre pron - tos   pa -   ra   Ti;*
-   *di - rá   sus   te - so - ros   a   Tus pies;*

There Are None Friendless 581 ⓕ

1. There are none friend-less, none a-fraid, The
sav - ing Truth who know, Their
shin - ing path leads from the shade, And

2. Truth sets us free from thought of sin; It
heals all sor - row's blight. Im -
mor - tal joy is found there - in, And

Proverbs 4:18 / II Corinthians 5:17 / Revelation 21:5; 22:5.

WORDS: William P. McKenzie, alt.
MUSIC: Jay Holcomb Frost

ANDALUCIA
C.M.
Alternate tune: 339

♩592 We Are Walking in the Light of God

Refrain

1. We are walk-ing in the light of God, We are walk-ing in the light of God. We are walk-ing in the light of God, We are walk-ing in the light of God.
2. We are pray-ing in the light of God, We are pray-ing in the light of God. We are pray-ing in the light of God, We are pray-ing in the light of God.
3. We are sing-ing in the light of God, We are sing-ing in the light of God. We are sing-ing in the light of God, We are sing-ing in the light of God.

Zulu Si - ya - hamb' e - ku - kha - nyen' kwen - khos', Si - ya - hamb' e - ku - kha - nyen' kwen - khos', Si - ya - hamb' e - ku - kha - nyen' kwen - khos', Si - ya - hamb' e - ku - kha - nyen' kwen - khos',

*Pronounced: See-yah-hahm-bah-ku-kah-nyen-kwen-kos

The refrain of this hymn comes from a well-known South African freedom song. New words, echoing the sense of unity and joy, have been added to create a large-scale refrain-verse-refrain-verse-refrain structure.

WORDS: Refrain Zulu; Eng. tr. Gracia Grindal; verses Désirée Goyette, alt.
MUSIC: Refrain South African melody; arr. *Freedom Is Coming*, 1984, keyboard arr. Ed Bogas; verse music Désirée Goyette, arr. Ed Bogas

SIYAHAMBA
12.12.12.13.Ref.

Verses

1. We are all   God's chil - dren,   ex -
2. As we turn   our fac - es,   up

pres-sions of   one Mind,   Liv-ing in   the ra -
to the light   of Life,   Har-mo-ny   re - plac -

- diance   of   Spir - it   all   di - vine.
- es   all   pain and   fear   and   strife.

Ev - ery heart   and na - tion   is
See the heaven - ly har - vest   so

to Refrain

an-swer-ing the call To a true sal - va-
boun-ti - ful - ly poured, As we raise our voic-

- tion know-ing God is All - in - all.
- es be - ing all of one ac - cord!

(fs) 594 We're Steadfastly Protected by Your Power

Von guten Mächten treu und still umgeben

English
1. We're stead-fast-ly pro-tec-ted by Your pow-er,
2. Your pure and qui-et love spreads o'er us deep-ly;

German
1. Von gu-ten Mäch-ten treu und still um-ge-ben,
2. Wenn sich die Stil-le nun tief um uns brei-tet,

En-cir-cled in the car-ing arms of Love.
We know Your full-ness now and feel Your peace.

be-hü-tet und ge-trö-stet wun-der-bar,
so lass uns hö-ren je-nen vol-len Klang

The words of this hymn are based on a poem by Dietrich Bonhoeffer, written in prison. One of the most important German theologians of the 20th century, he was executed in 1945 as a result of his courageous resistance to Nazi fascism. His book *The Cost of Discipleship* is still widely read today.

WORDS: Dietrich Bonhoeffer; Eng. tr. and adapt. CSPS
MUSIC: Otto Abel; arr. CSPS
11.10.11.10.Ref.

Eng. tr. © 2017 The Christian Science Board of Directors
Music © Verlag Merseburger

When My Heart Is Lost in Sorrow 595 (fs)

1. When my heart is lost in sor - row, and light seems far and
2. When wea - ri - ness en - gulfs me, dis - cour - age - ment sinks
3. When my days feel much too bus - y to find where prayer fits

dim, There's a ten - der prayer I can al - ways pray:
in, There's a hope - ful prayer I can al - ways pray:
in, There's a time - less prayer I can al - ways pray:

Refrain

Sim - ply prais - ing Him. Praise the cre - a - tor. Let
Sim - ply prais - ing Him. Praise the cre - a - tor. Let
Sim - ply prais - ing Him. Praise the cre - a - tor. Let

Psalms 96:1; 103:1.

WORDS: Susan Booth Mack Snipes, alt.
MUSIC: Susan Booth Mack Snipes; arr. Sue Loomis and Robert Rockabrand

SANCHEZ
Irregular

⒡599 Whither Shall I Go from Thy Spirit

The music arrangement given here is based upon the version sung, a cappella, at the Adventure Unlimited (A/U) Ranches; a simple accompaniment and guitar chords have been added. The hymn may be sung twice, with the descant included the second time through.

WORDS: Psalms 139:7–10; desc. Psalms 46:10 and scriptural para.
MUSIC: Mark Shepherd; desc. anon.; transc. and arr. CSPS

WHITHER
Irregular

ABOUT THIS 2017 HYMNAL

The goal of this hymnal is that its hymns be accessible to as many people as possible while also offering metaphysical and musical integrity. As congregational songs, the melodies are in a comfortable singing range. Hymns with more complicated forms are presented as clearly as possible. And the accompaniments are musically substantial without being unnecessarily difficult.

Musicians perusing this volume might observe that some of the hymns are equally well suited to the organ or the piano, while others are more idiomatic to the piano. A separate Musician's Edition is available in which these considerations are addressed more fully, with special notations to assist organists with the hymns originally intended for piano accompaniment. The Musician's Edition also contains designated organ arrangements alongside piano versions of select hymns.

Adjustments to hymn texts are sometimes made in order to bring a poem into conformity with hymn conventions, particularly uniform syllable and emphasis structure from verse to verse. At times, language is updated, especially when an older text is joined to a newer tune. In the compilation of this hymnal, these procedures have not been followed mechanically; all decisions have been carefully weighed on a case-by-case basis. Very small changes have sometimes been made to existing tunes in order to bring them into agreement with a selected text. Care has been taken to ensure that these changes have not altered the character of the music.

The Order and Presentation of the Hymns

Like the 1932 *Christian Science Hymnal*, the hymns in this volume are arranged as nearly as possible in alphabetical order according to their first lines. Because this hymnal incorporates most of the hymns from the 2008 *Christian Science Hymnal Supplement: Hymns 430–462*, the hymn numbers in this volume begin at 430. For ease of use, each hymn carries a title corresponding to the first line. Where appropriate, and where space permits, guitar chords are given.

Some hymns originated in a language other than English. Where possible and practical, the original language is included alongside the English translation. Most of the English translations presented here were created specifically for this volume.

Of special consideration is the inclusion of three alternative tunes joined with the words of the Communion Doxology. Mary Baker Eddy took care to shape the words of the Doxology, as found on page 126 of the *Manual of The Mother Church*; however, while often associated with the tune OLD HUNDREDTH, it may be sung to these alternative tunes. The first alternative tune for the Doxology text (Hymn 445) also gives translations of the words in 16 different languages. This, along with many hymns from around the world contained within this hymnal, underscores the global reach of Christian Science and demonstrates "the Church Universal and Triumphant" (*Manual*, p. 19).

The Hymn Page

Page 367 provides a diagram labeling the various components of the hymn page (hymn number, title, etc.). In some cases, historical, contextual, or performance notes are included beneath the music. Included here are scriptural citations indicating the biblical source of many of the words and themes within the hymns. These scriptural citations are not exhaustive, but are helpful in pointing users toward the Bible.

Beneath the solid horizontal line at the bottom of each hymn page lies a wealth of information. On the left-hand side:

- **Words attribution:** identifying the author or literary source, along with, when applicable, the translator, adaptor, or other contributor to the text.
- **Music attribution:** identifying the composer or source of the music, along with, as appropriate, the harmonizer, arranger, or other musical contributor.

In some cases, modifiers were added to these attributions to give a sense of the editorial work behind the words and music.

- **Alt. (altered):** When applied to the words, this indicates a small change, often to update the language or preserve the rhyme scheme. When applied to the music, this, similarly, indicates a minor change.
- **Adapt. (adapted):** When applied to the words, this indicates a significant change of meaning, often to bring the text into accord with Christian Science thought. When applied to the music, this indicates that it has been changed in order to accommodate the text.

Below the horizontal line, on the right-hand side:

- **Tune Name:** (in all caps) identifying the name of the melody.
- **Meter:** identifying the meter of the hymn.
- **Alternative tune:** listing, by hymn number, alternative tunes within the 2017 *Hymnal* or the 1932 *Hymnal* that set the same text (when applicable).
- **Alternative arr.:** listing, by hymn number, alternative arrangements of the same tune found in either the 2017 *Hymnal* or the 1932 *Hymnal* (when applicable).

Finally, abbreviated copyright notices are given for all materials currently under copyright protection. Full copyright notices are given in the Index of Copyright Acknowledgments.

461   Come unto Me

1. Come un-to me, you wea-ry, And I will give you rest.
2. Come un-to me, you wan-derers, And I will give you light.

1. Hymn number
2. Guitar chords
3. Title
4. Scriptural reference
5. Attributions

6. Copyright notice
7. Informational note
8. Hymn tune
9. Hymn meter
10. Cross reference

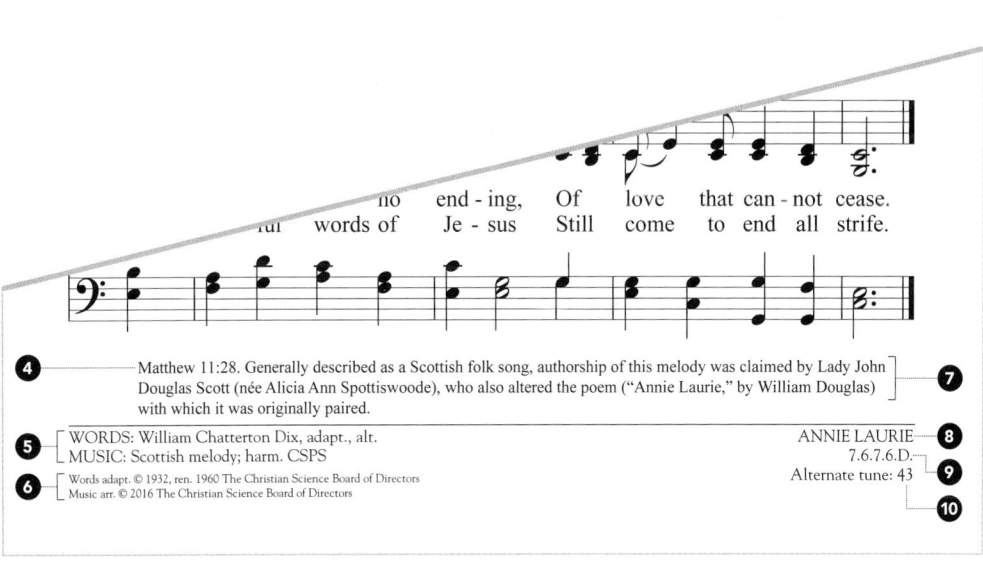

... no end - ing, Of love that can - not cease.
... words of Je - sus Still come to end all strife.

Matthew 11:28. Generally described as a Scottish folk song, authorship of this melody was claimed by Lady John Douglas Scott (née Alicia Ann Spottiswoode), who also altered the poem ("Annie Laurie," by William Douglas) with which it was originally paired.

WORDS: William Chatterton Dix, adapt., alt.
MUSIC: Scottish melody; harm. CSPS

Words adapt. © 1932, ren. 1960 The Christian Science Board of Directors
Music arr. © 2016 The Christian Science Board of Directors

ANNIE LAURIE
7.6.7.6.D.
Alternate tune: 43

INDEXES

Copyright Acknowledgments

Listed here are the names and addresses of copyright owners and administrators whose works appear in this *Hymnal*. The publisher has obtained permission from copyright owners to include their materials in this *Hymnal* only, and no further use may be made without obtaining permission from the copyright holder.

Extensive effort has been made to determine and locate the copyright owners of the materials that appear in the *Christian Science Hymnal: Hymns 430–603*. The Publisher welcomes reports of inaccurate copyright notices or omissions, and will gladly correct subsequent printings. The public domain status of materials are not noted on individual pages or in the Copyright Acknowledgments.

A purchaser of this *Hymnal* may reproduce a hymn in this volume that is copyrighted solely by The Christian Science Board of Directors, provided that:

- it is a one-time use, e.g., for a special service or meeting;
- the copyright notice as shown on the page is included on the reproduction;
- the *Christian Science Hymnal: Hymns 430–603* is acknowledged as the source; and
- not more than 100 copies are made.

All other requests for permission should be made in writing to **permissions@csps.com**.

Abingdon Press (See Music Services)

Alfred Music, 10214 USA Today Way, Miramar, FL 33025 – (954) 213-6018 – permissions@alfred.com – www.alfred.com

Allen, Peter B., 1708 Norte Way, Santa Rosa, CA 95404 – pba007@me.com

Asian Institute for Liturgy and Music (See Sambalikhaan Foundation)

Augsburg Fortress Publishers, P.O. Box 1209, Minneapolis, MN 55440-1209 – (800) 421-0239 – copyright@augsburgfortress.org – www.augsburgfortress.org

Badejo, Emmanuel, c/o Catholic Diocese Of Oyo, Sawmill Mariama Road, Oyo, P.M.B 1480, Oyo State, Nigeria – oyodiocese@yahoo.com – contactus@catholicdioceseoyo.org

Belwin-Mills Publishing Corp. (See Alfred Music)

Bennetts, Fenella, Greenfield, Manor Road, Ripley, Surrey GU23 6JW, UK – fenella@fbennetts.co.uk

Borges, Dagmar (copyright owner address unknown)

Brethren Press, 1451 Dundee Avenue, Elgin, IL 60120-1694 brethrenpress@brethren.org – www.brethrenpress.com

Brewis, Andrew D., 13 Ambleside Avenue, Walton on Thames, Surrey KT12 3LW, UK – info@notedformusic.com, andrew@brewisfamily.uk

Bridgestone Multimedia Group, 300 N. McKemy Avenue, Chandler, AZ 85226 – (866) 774-3774 – www.gobmg.com

Buckley Jr., James J., 33B Purchase Street, Milford, MA 01757-1652

Capitol CMG Publishing, P.O. Box 5085, 101 Winners Circle, Brentwood, TN 37024-5085 – licensing@capitolcmgpublishing.com – www.capitolcmgpublishing.com

Carl Fischer, LLC, 48 Wall Street, 28th Floor, New York, NY 10005 – (212) 777-0900 – www.carlfischer.com

CCCM Music (See Capitol CMG Publishing)

Christian Science Board of Directors, The, Permissions, The First Church of Christ, Scientist, 210 Massachusetts Avenue, Boston, MA 02115 – permissions@csps.com

Historic Church of the Ascension (See Episcopal Diocese of New Jersey)

Cooper, Charlene Moore, c/o Dr. Valerie C. Cooper, Duke University Divinity School, Box 90968, Durham, NC 27708-0967

E. C. Schirmer Music Company, 1727 Larkin Williams Road, Fenton, MO 63026-2024 – (800) 647-2117 – www.ecspublishing.com

ECS Publishing (See E. C. Schirmer)

Episcopal Diocese of New Jersey, 808 W. State Street, Trenton, NJ 08618 – (609) 394-5281 – info@dioceseofnj.org – www.dioceseofnj.org

Fines, David, 1847 Rue Cartier, Longueuil, QC J4K 4E3 Canada – David.fines@gmail.com

Fraysse, Claude (See Patrik Fraysse)

Fraysse, Patrik, 990, Allée de la Grande Musenne, 26750 Genissieux, France Patrik fraysse@gmail.com

Fred Bock Music Company, Inc., 125 South Louis Avenue, 2nd Floor, Glendale, CA 91205 – (818) 551-0800 – info@fredbock.com – www.fredbock.com

G. Schirmer, Inc. (See Music Sales)

GBGMusik (See General Board of Global Ministries)

GIA Publications, Inc., 7404 S. Mason Avenue, Chicago, IL 60638 – (800) 442-1358 – reprints@giamusic.com – www.giamusic.com

Gacías, Javier, c/o Monica Sevil, Mezquuida, Abogado ICAM 52.316, Madrid, Spain – monica@rosevil.es

General Board of Global Ministries/GBGMusik, 458 Ponce de Leon Avenue, Atlanta, GA 30308 – copyright@umcmission.org – www.umcmission.org

Gerth Medien Musikverlag GmbH, Dillerberg 1, 35614 Asslar-Berghausen, Germany – www.gerth.de

Glaser, Eliot, 2943 South Detroit Avenue, Tulsa, OK 74114 – eg@eliotglaser.com

H. W. Gray Company, The (See Alfred Music)

Hal Leonard LLC, 7777 W. Bluemound Road, P.O. Box 13819, Milwaukee, WI 53213 – (414) 774-3630 – publishingperm@halleonard.com – www.halleonard.com

Hay, Violet (copyright owner address unknown)

Hernandez, Frank (See Bridgestone Media Group)

Hinshaw Music, Inc. (See Fred Bock Music)

Hope Publishing Company, 380 S. Main Place, Carol Stream, IL 60188 – (800) 323-1049 – (630) 665-3200 – permissions@hopepublishing.com – www.hopepublishing.com

Hymnal Project, The (See Brethren Press)

In Our Field Productions, c/o The Solo Committee, 2136 N Lakecrest Loop, Hernando, FL 34442 – solocommittee3@gmail.com

Jan-Lee Music, P.O. Box 1210, Penn Valley, CA 94965 – (800) 211-8454 – tache@together.net – www.jan-leemusic.com

Lightchild Publishing, 477 Cascade Drive, Mill Valley, CA 94941 – desimuse@earthlink.net

Luíz da Silva, Gelson, Rua Carlos Lacerda, 385, Bairro Trevo, CWP 31545-070, Belo Horizonte-MG, Brazil

Marashin, Jaci (Estate of), c/o Ana Dulce Maraschin, Rua Frei Caneca 425, Apt. 71, 01307-001 Sao Paulo, SP, Brazil – adp.maraschin@hotmail.com

McCarter, Kevin, (information withheld)

Möseler Verlag, Hoffman-von-Fallersleben-Str. 8, 38304 Wolfenbüttel , Germany – info@ moeseler-verlag.de – www.moeseler-verlag.de

Music Sales, G. Schirmer, Inc., 1247 Sixth Street, Santa Monica, CA 90401 – (310) 393-9900 – info@musicsales.com – www.musicsales.com

Music Services, 5409 Maryland Way, Suite 200, Brentwood, TN 37027 – (615) 371-1320 – www.musicservices.org

Navias, Eugene B. (See Buckley, James J.)

Nkuinji, Abel, 3615 Rue Victor Hugo, 92 700 Colombes, France – abelnkuinji@yahoo.fr

Novello & Company, Ltd. (See Music Sales)

Oxford University Press, Great Clarendon Street, Oxford OX2 6DP, England – WebEnquiry.UK@oup.com – www.global.oup.com

Peace of Music Publishing AB (See GIA Publications, Inc.)

Peermusic III, Ltd. (See Hal Leonard LLC)

Pilgrim Press, The, 700 Prospect Avenue, Cleveland, OH 44115 – (216) 736-3766 – permissions@thepilgrimpress.com – www.thepilgrimpress.com

R.D. Row Music Company, Inc. (See Carl Fischer, LLC)

Rice, Gene (copyright owner address unknown)

Rung-Keller, Paul Sophus (Estate of), c/o Maggie Palludan, Hans Edvard Teglers Vej 11, DK-2920 Charlottenlund, Denmark – maggiedoo@gmail.dk

Sambalikhaan Foundation, Asian Institute for Liturgy and Music, 275 E. Rodriguez Boulevard, Cathedral Heights, Quezon City, Philippines – info@sambalikhaan.org – www.sambalikhaan.org

Savgos Music, Inc. (See Hal Leonard LLC)

Taylor, Edwin R., 34 Spring Hill Lane, Bethel, CT 06801-2724

Tindall, Adrienne M., c/o P O Box 5018, Vernon Hills, IL 60061 – a.tindall@comcast.net

United Church of Canada (See Wood Lake Books)

United Methodist Publishing House, The (See Music Services)

Universal Music-Brentwood Benson Publ. (See Capitol CMG Publishing)

Van Ness Press, Inc. (See Music Services)

Verlag Merseburger Berlin BmbH, Naumburger Straße 40, 34127 Kassel, Germany – www.merseburger.de

WGRG, Iona Community (See GIA Publications, Inc.)

Walton Music Corp. (See GIA Publications, Inc.)

Wood Lake Books, 485 Beaver Lake Road, Kelowna, BC V4V 1S5, Canada – (250) 766-2778 – www.woodlakebooks.com

World Library Publications, 3708 River Road, Suite 400, Franklin Park, IL 60131-2158 – (800) 621-5197 – wlpreprint@jspaluch.com – www.wlpmusic.com

430 Words © 1932, renewed 1960 The Christian Science Board of Directors.
Music © 2017 The Christian Science Board of Directors.

431 Words adaptation © 1932, renewed 1960 The Christian Science Board of Directors.
Music © 2017 The Christian Science Board of Directors.

432 French Words, English translation, Music arrangement © 2016 The Christian Science Board of Directors.

433 Music arrangement and descant © 2017 The Christian Science Board of Directors.

434 Words © 1955, 1956 The Christian Science Board of Directors.
Words adaptation © 1997, 2014, 2017 The Christian Science Board of Directors.
Music © 1997 Adrienne M. Tindall.

435 Words and Music © Abel Nkuinji.
English translation © 2004 General Board of Global Ministries.

436 Words and Music © Möseler Verlag, Wolfenbuttel. Permission sought.

437 Words adaptation © 2008 Fenella Bennetts.
Music © 1938 Novello & Company, Limited. All rights reserved. International copyright secured.

438 Music arrangement © 2008 The Christian Science Board of Directors.

439 Words © 1992 GIA Publications, Incorporated. All rights reserved. Used by permission.
Music harmonization © 2017 The Christian Science Board of Directors.

440 Words © 1932, renewed 1960 The Christian Science Board of Directors.
Music © 2016 The Christian Science Board of Directors.

441 Music © 2017 The Christian Science Board of Directors.

442 Music harmonization © 1989 Hope Publishing Company, Carol Stream, IL 60188. All rights reserved. Used by permission.

443 German Words, English translation, Music © 2016 The Christian Science Board of Directors.

444 Words © 1987 The Christian Science Board of Directors.
Words alteration and Music © 2017 The Christian Science Board of Directors.

445 Words translations: Danish © 1957, renewed 1985, Dutch © 1946, renewed 1974, Finnish © 2017, French © 1948, renewed 1976, German © 1916, 1955, renewed 1944, 1983, Greek © 1974, Igbo © 2017, Iluko © 2017, Indonesian © 1979, Japanese © 1971, Norwegian © 1959, renewed 1987, Polish © 2001, Portuguese © 1968, renewed 1996, Russian © 1997, Spanish © 1946, renewed 1974, Swedish © 1929 renewed 1957 The Christian Science Board of Directors.

446 Music arrangement © 2016 The Christian Science Board of Directors.

447 Music © 2017 The Christian Science Board of Directors.

448 Words and Music © 1995 Gene Rice and Charlene Moore Cooper.

Tunes, Alphabetical

Tunes, Metrical

Tempo Indications

Authors, Composers, and Sources

Dates are not included for contemporary authors and composers.

Languages Other than English

Danish
445 O Du, vor Gud, ophøjet vær
(Be Thou, O God)

Dutch
445 O God, ons loflied rijze omhoog
(Be Thou, O God)

Ewe
483 Elolo nye Mawu elolo ŋutɔ
(God guards me)

Finnish
445 Sun kunniaasi julistaa
(Be Thou, O God)

French
516 C'est vrai: Dieu est bon
(It's true: God is good)
445 Glorie au Très-Haut, à l'Éternel !
(Be Thou, O God)
562 Je louerai l'Eternel
(Praise, I will praise You, Lord)
473 Père-Mère Dieu
(Father-Mother God, All-in-all)
432 Plutôt que tous les gains
(Above all earthly gain)
435 Tout est fait pour la gloire de
Dieu
(All is done for the glory of God)

German
436 Alles ist eitel
(All may seem vain)
476 Banges Herz, leg deine Sorge
(Fearful heart, put all your cares)
522 Macht hoch die Tür
(Lift up the door)
549 O du fröhliche, o du selige
(O thou joyful, O thou blessed)
443 Sei gütig und rein
(Be gentle, be pure)

594 Von guten Mächten treu und still
umgeben
(We're steadfastly protected by
Your power)
445 Wir preisen Dich, GOTT, unsrem
Herrn!
(Be Thou, O God)

Greek
445 Κύριε, η δόξα Σου τρανή
(Be Thou, O God)

Igbo
445 K'ebulie G'elu Chine-ke
(Be Thou, O God)

Iluko
445 O. Apo Diosmi iti natan-ok
(Be Thou, O God)

Indonesian
445 Tuhan, bagiMu pujian
(Be Thou, O God)

Itneg
578 (Sing a song, sing a song to God)

Japanese
445 いと高き神よ
(Be Thou, O God)

Norwegian
445 Vær høyt oppohøtet, Du, vår Gud
(Be Thou, O God)

Polish
445 „Bądź uwielbiony, Ojcze nasz!
(Be Thou, O God)

Portuguese
582 A graça do Senhor
(The grace of God)
482 Deus criou o homen de Si mesmo
(God created us in His own
image)

504 Eu quero a Verdade conhecer
(I want to know the truth that
Jesus taught us)
445 Louvado sejas Tu, ó Deus!
(Be Thou, O God)
532 Que Deus nos abençoe
(May God give us Her blessing)

Russian
445 Возвысим, Господи, Тебя
(Be Thou, O God)

Spanish
517 Canto de alegría
(Joyfully we're singing)
555 El amor, el amor
(Only love, only love)
493 El cielo canta alegría
(Heaven is singing for joy)
445 Enaltecido seas, Tú
(Be Thou, O God)
586 Éste es el día
(This is the day)
455 Oh, bajo Tu ala tutelar
(Brood o'er us with Thy
shelt'ring wing)
484 Oro aquí con Dios
(God is here with me)
580 Ten mi vida
(Take my life, and let it be)

Swedish
445 Dig, Herre Gud, upphöja vi
(Be Thou, O God)

Xhosa
557 Mayenziwe 'ntando yakho
(Our Father-Mother, Your will
be done)

Zulu
592 Siyahamba
(We are walking in the light of
God)

First Lines and Common Titles

Hymns by Mary Baker Eddy are printed in italics.